Timely Tasks
for
Fast Finishers

9–11 Year Olds

Peter Clutterbuck

Brilliant Publications

We hope you and your pupils enjoy using this book. You might be interested in these other books published by Brilliant Publications:

Timely Tasks: 5–7 Year Olds	978-1-905780-00-6
Timely Tasks: 7–9 Year Olds	978-1-905780-01-3
Brilliant Activities for Gifted and Talented Children	978-1-903853-47-4
Thinking Strategies for the Successful Classroom: 5–7 Year Olds	978-1-905780-03-7
Thinking Strategies for the Successful Classroom: 7–9 Year Olds	978-1-905780-04-4
Thinking Strategies for the Successful Classroom: 9–11 Year Olds	978-1-905780-05-1

If you would like further information on these or other titles published by Brilliant Publications, please look at our website www.brilliantpublications.co.uk or write to the address below.

Published in the UK by Brilliant Publications

Sales:

BEBC (Brilliant Publications)
Albion Close, Parkstone, Poole, Dorset BH12 3LL
Tel: 0845 1309200   01202 712910
Fax: 0845 1309300
e-mail: brilliant@bebc.co.uk
website: www.brilliantpublications.co.uk

Editorial and Marketing:

10 Church View, Sparrow Hall Farm, Edlesborough, Dunstable,
Bedfordshire LU6 2ES
Tel: 01525 222292

The name Brilliant Publications and its logo are registered trademarks.

Written by Peter Clutterbuck
Typeset and designed by Bob Reyes
Illustrations by Greg Anderson-Clift
Cover by Lynda Murray
Text copyright © Peter Clutterbuck 2001
© 2001 BLAKE PUBLISHING

This edition is for sale in the United Kingdom only. Originally published in Australia by Blake Publishing.

ISBN 978-1-905780-02-0

Printed 2007 in the UK
10   9   8   7   6   5   4   3   2   1

CONTENTS

Task Cards

Story writing

Write a story about a dinosaur without using the letter E in any of the words.

_____

_____

_____

_____

_____

_____

_____

Use another sheet of paper if you need more space.

5 MINUTES

Tricky proverbs

The letters in these proverbs are in their correct order but not grouped correctly. Can you work out what each proverb is? The first part of number 1 is done for you.

1. As malll eakwi llsin kagr eats hip.

   A small leak
   _____

2. Ever yclo udh asas ilve rlin ing.

   _____

3. Gre atoa ksfr omli ttl eaco rnsg row.

   _____

4. Afr ien din nee dis afr ien dind eed.

   _____

5 MINUTES

ENGLISH

Brilliant Publications

© Blake Publishing

Meanings

If the words in the following pairs are similar, write YES.
If they are opposite to each other, write NO.
If they have no obvious connection, write X.

1.	straight	bent	_____	9.	broad	wide	_____
2.	buy	sell	_____	10.	tall	silly	_____
3.	plentiful	ample	_____	11.	margin	edge	_____
4.	old	table	_____	12.	cease	stop	_____
5.	summit	top	_____	13.	jewel	gem	_____
6.	finish	end	_____	14.	strong	weak	_____
7.	sharp	new	_____				
8.	sour	sweet	_____				

5 MINUTES

Letterbox

1.	M	T	A	E	R	O
2.	E	O	T	R	M	T
3.	W	Y	X	B	Y	E
4.	M	T	Q	P	X	T
5.	V	Y	W	S	T	V
6.	A	P	U	E	I	O

1. Which line contains the most letters that come after R in the alphabet? _____

2. What letter is always to the right of M in the letterbox? _____

3. What vowel occurs the most times? _____

4. Which line contains all the vowels? _____

5. Which lines contain only consonants? _____

6. Make four words from the first four letters in the first row.

5 MINUTES

ENGLISH

Scrambled dorws!

In five minutes, can you unscramble these common words? You might find it takes just as long to do the last five as it does the first 15!

1. ymept _____
2. lhwee _____
3. emsil _____
4. dofun _____
5. yadis _____
6. lacme _____
7. refve _____

8. yaprt _____
9. tahbi _____
10. mtsor _____
11. nabco _____
12. prgou _____
13. eohrs _____
14. dpsee _____

15. nimde _____
16. garny _____
17. mhotu _____
18. ewtir _____
19. tirna _____
20. ebetle _____

5 MINUTES

Arithmetic

All the words fitting the clues can be made from the letters of

A R I T H M E T I C .

What are the words?

1. a good friend _____
2. a female horse _____
3. you sit on it _____
4. not wild _____
5. a group of footballers _____
6. the organ that pumps blood _____
7. the fat of milk _____
8. small rodent _____
9. drop of liquid from the eye _____

5 MINUTES

ENGLISH

Brilliant Publications

Timely Tasks for Fast Finishers 9–11 Year Olds
© Blake Publishing

Word play

Take one letter from the first word and place it in the second word to form two words with similar meanings, for example curt / cave = cut / carve.

1. flat / pump _____ / _____

2. shred / ban _____ / _____

3. boast / hip _____ / _____

4. blare / bad _____ / _____

5. skill / laughter _____ / _____

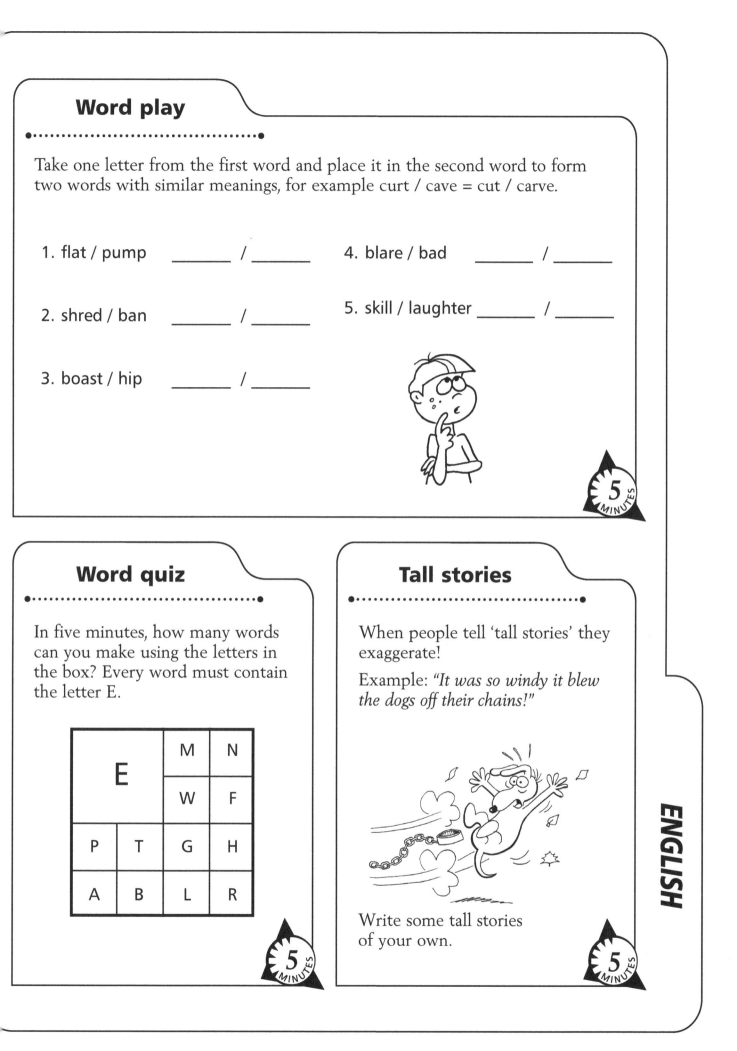

Word quiz

In five minutes, how many words can you make using the letters in the box? Every word must contain the letter E.

E	M	N
	W	F
P	T	G	H
A	B	L	R

Tall stories

When people tell 'tall stories' they exaggerate!

Example: *"It was so windy it blew the dogs off their chains!"*

Write some tall stories of your own.

Brilliant Publications

This page may be reproduced by the original purchaser for non-commercial classroom use.

Timely Tasks for Fast Finishers 9–11 Year Olds

© Blake Publishing

7

ENGLISH

Mystery words

Can you work out the mystery word below?

First work out the smaller words using the clues given.

Write the correct letter in the space beside each number.

Then match that letter with the corresponding number in the mystery word to find out what the mystery word is.

Clues:

1. Grass in your garden:	3	2	6	9	
2. Part of the foot:	1	7	7	4	
3. What a mouse lives in:	1	5	3	8	
4. The world's largest mammal:	6	1	2	3	8

Mystery word: 1   2   3   4   5   6   7   8   9

5 MINUTES

Cross it out!

Cross out the word in each line which *cannot* be made from the letters in the word in capitals that begins that line. Each letter can be used only once.

ARITHMETIC	cream	heart	hearse	mate	came
FORTNIGHT	tonight	nought	tight	fright	thing
CREATURE	create	tear	trace	curate	centre
PARADISE	draper	praise	spire	parade	spider
CONSISTENTLY	silent	costly	sister	scones	scent

2 MINUTES

ENGLISH

8

Brilliant Publications

This page may be reproduced by the original purchaser for non-commercial classroom use.

Timely Tasks for Fast Finishers 9–11 Year Olds

© Blake Publishing

Missing EEs

Two *Es* are missing from each of these words. Can you put them back correctly?

1. agl   (bird) _____

2. jwl   (precious stone) _____

3. fnc   (barrier) _____

4. gnral (army rank) _____

5. nmy   (foe) _____

6. vlvt   (soft cloth) _____

7. prfct (ideal) _____

8. coff   (beverage) _____

Missing creatures

Can you name the creatures whose names end with these words?
The first one has been done for you.

1. _____ pie   magpie

2. _____ rich   _____

3. _____ key   _____

4. _____ rot   _____

5. _____ pine   _____

6. _____ at   _____

7. _____ out   _____

8. _____ use   _____

ENGLISH

Brilliant Publications

This page may be reproduced by the original purchaser for non-commercial classroom use.

Timely Tasks for Fast Finishers 9–11 Year Olds

© Blake Publishing

9

Shrinking words

Drop one letter at a time to make another word. Each time you take away a letter, the remaining letters must spell a real word.

Example: gasps ⟶ gaps ⟶ gas ⟶ as ⟶ a

Now try these:

S T A R T L I N G

↓ _____
↓ _____
↓ _____
↓ _____
↓ _____
↓ _____
↓ _____
↓ _____

S N O W I N G

↓ _____
↓ _____
↓ _____
↓ _____
↓ _____
↓ _____

Multiple poems

How many times can you rearrange these words from a famous poem? You must use all the words each time and your sentences must make sense.

"The ploughman homeward plods his weary way."

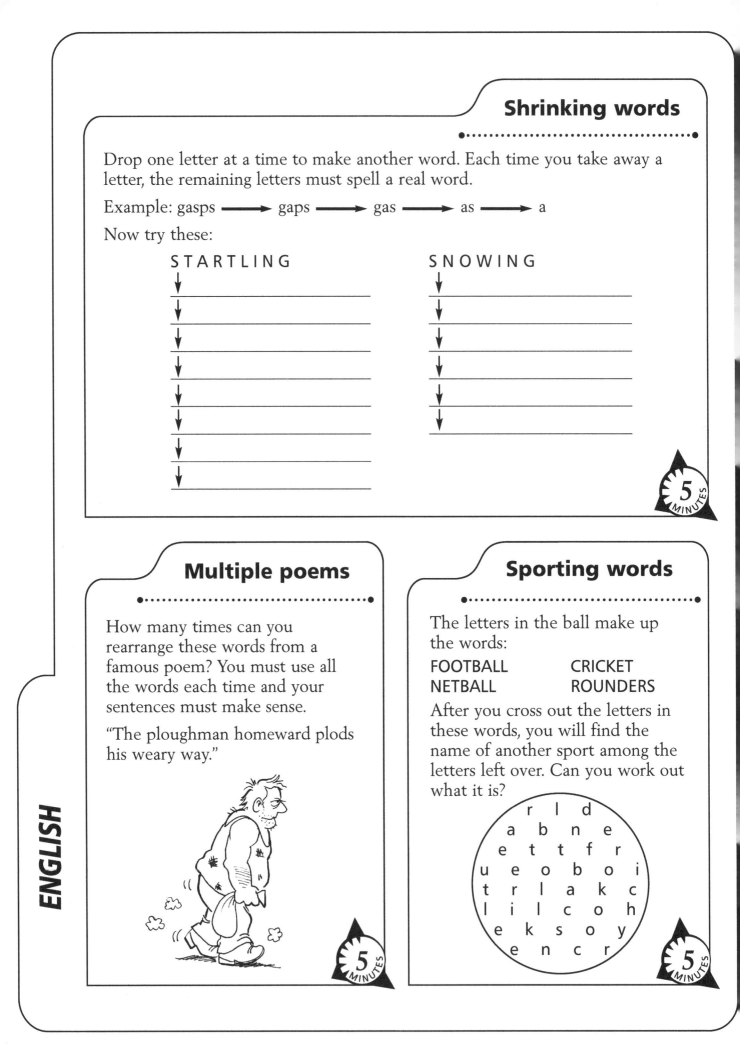

Sporting words

The letters in the ball make up the words:

FOOTBALL   CRICKET
NETBALL   ROUNDERS

After you cross out the letters in these words, you will find the name of another sport among the letters left over. Can you work out what it is?

r l d
a b n e
e t t f r
u e o b o i
t r l a k c
l i l c o h
e k s o y
e n c r

10

Brilliant Publications
This page may be reproduced by the original purchaser for non-commercial classroom use.

Timely Tasks for Fast Finishers 9–11 Year Olds
© Blake Publishing

ENGLISH

Swap shops

A shop owner asks her workers to stand in the street and advertise what her shop sells.

The shop does not sell HOSES. One person is standing in the wrong place. What does the shop sell?

2 MINUTES

Growing sentences

Write a sentence in which:
- the first word has only one letter
- the second has two letters
- the third has three letters ... and so on.

Example: *"I am the last named father!"*

3 MINUTES

Therein

How many words can you find in the word T H E R E I N ?

The letters must stay in the same order. You should be able to find eight.

1. _____   5. _____

2. _____   6. _____

3. _____   7. _____

4. _____   8. _____

3 MINUTES

ENGLISH

© Blake Publishing

Scrapbook

Using the letters in the word 'Scrapbook', find the words to match the clues below. You may use a letter in any word only as often as it occurs in 'scrapbook'.

1. Chef: _____

2. We wear it on our feet: _____

3. Sea creature: _____

4. A tree that has acorns: _____

5. A male pig: _____

6. A hooded snake: _____

7. A large stone: _____

8. Automobile: _____

9. A grassed area to picnic in: _____

10. Police officer: _____

11. Thief: _____

12. Type of fish: _____

10 MINUTES

Word web

How many words can you find in the web below? Start at any letter and follow the threads to make your words.

5 MINUTES

What's it say?

Do you know what each of these acronyms stands for? Write the full meaning of each.

V.C.R.   N.A.S.A.

L.C.D.   D.I.Y.

G.M.T.   O.A.P.

H.G.V.   A.S.B.O.

5 MINUTES

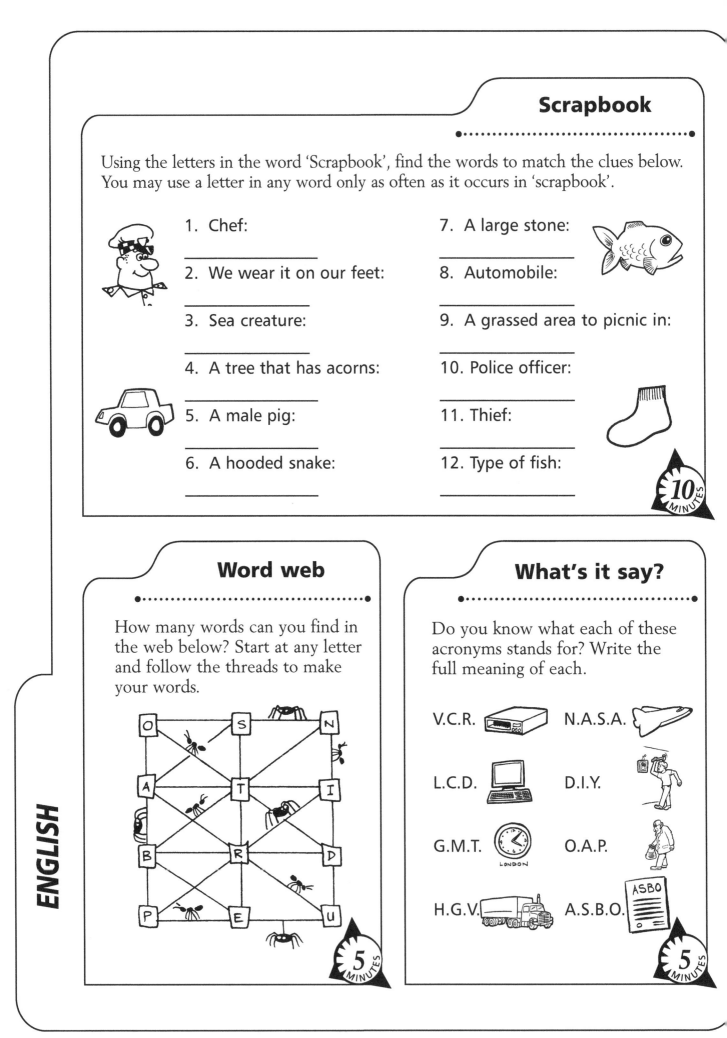

12

Brilliant Publications

This page may be reproduced by the original purchaser for non-commercial classroom use.

Timely Tasks for Fast Finishers 9–11 Year Olds

© Blake Publishing

ENGLISH

Dictionary daze

Use your dictionary to answer these questions. Give the meanings of each word.

? 1. What is the longest word beginning with 'ex'?

2. What word directly follows 'lollipop'?

3. What word comes directly before 'rhinoceros'?

4. What is the very last word in your dictionary?

5. What is the fifth word in the 'in' section?

5 MINUTES

Mixed-up meals

Tommy's shopping list was accidentally torn in half. Match the beginnings and endings so Tommy knows what to buy.

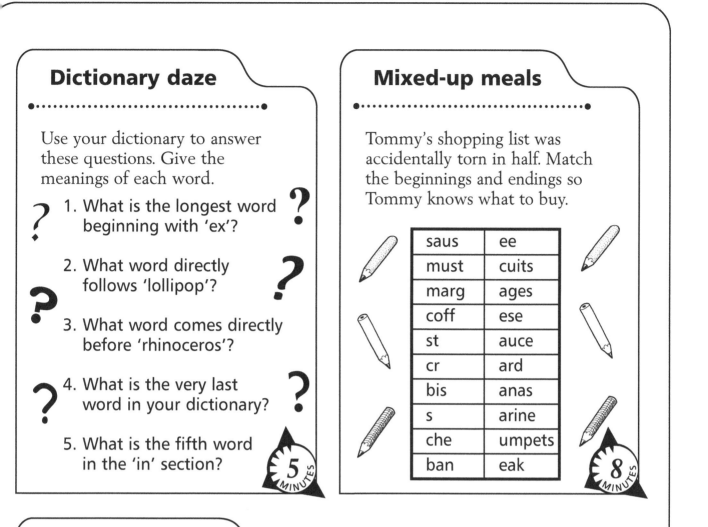

saus	ee
must	cuits
marg	ages
coff	ese
st	auce
cr	ard
bis	anas
s	arine
che	umpets
ban	eak

8 MINUTES

Connections

Each word in the box has a partner in the list below.

Write the partners beside each other.

ice	hay	terrier	cheese	heart
hornet	nephew	plant	vinegar	adder

1. foliage _____

2. insect _____

3. yoghurt _____

4. niece _____

5. olive oil _____

6. reptile _____

7. dalmatian _____

8. meadow _____

9. cardiologist _____

10. glacier _____

5 MINUTES

ENGLISH

Brilliant Publications

This page may be reproduced by the original purchaser for non-commercial classroom use.

Timely Tasks for Fast Finishers 9–11 Year Olds

© Blake Publishing

13

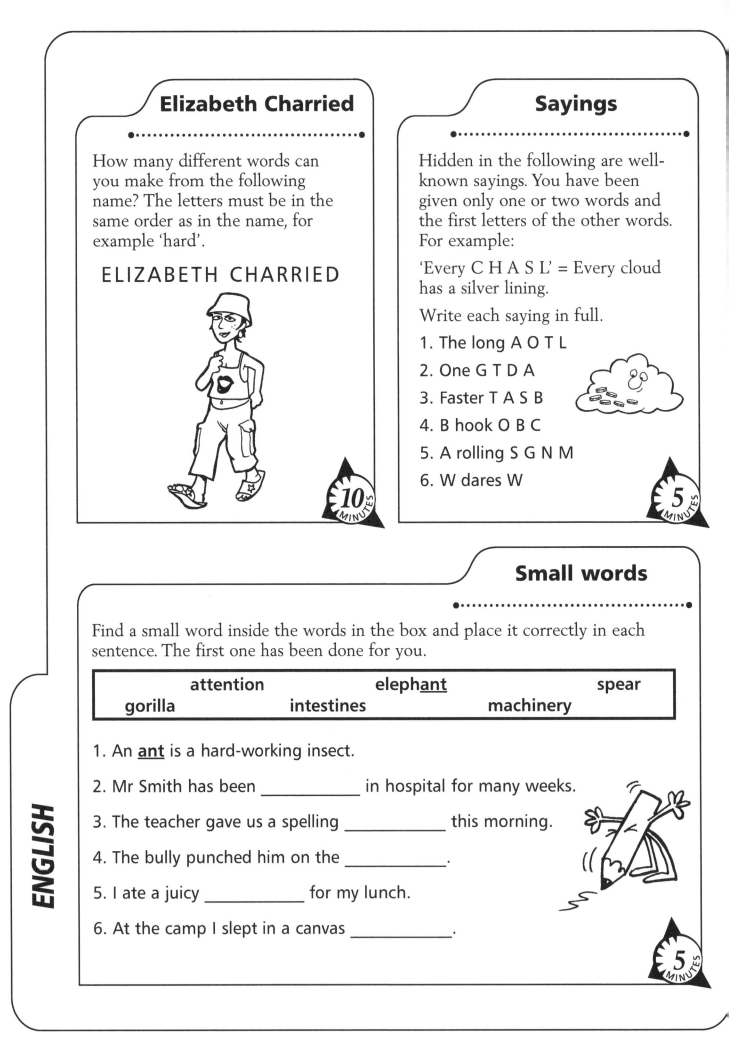

Elizabeth Charried

How many different words can you make from the following name? The letters must be in the same order as in the name, for example 'hard'.

ELIZABETH CHARRIED

Sayings

Hidden in the following are well-known sayings. You have been given only one or two words and the first letters of the other words. For example:

'Every C H A S L' = Every cloud has a silver lining.

Write each saying in full.

1. The long A O T L
2. One G T D A
3. Faster T A S B
4. B hook O B C
5. A rolling S G N M
6. W dares W

Small words

Find a small word inside the words in the box and place it correctly in each sentence. The first one has been done for you.

attention	elephant	spear
gorilla	intestines	machinery

1. An **ant** is a hard-working insect.

2. Mr Smith has been _____ in hospital for many weeks.

3. The teacher gave us a spelling _____ this morning.

4. The bully punched him on the _____.

5. I ate a juicy _____ for my lunch.

6. At the camp I slept in a canvas _____.

Brilliant Publications
This page may be reproduced by the original purchaser for non-commercial classroom use.

Timely Tasks for Fast Finishers 9–11 Year Olds
© Blake Publishing

ENGLISH

Fill in the blanks

How many words can you find by filling in the letter blanks?

If you can find more than 25 give yourself a pat on the back.

_____ _____ _____ S T

Country cultures

Draw lines between the words and the countries they are related to.

turban	New Zealand
castanets	India
Zulu	Spain
moussaka	Scotland
kiwi	South Africa
loch	Greece
taco	Italy
spaghetti	Mexico

Word changes

In each column, make the top word into the bottom word by changing one letter at a time. Each step must make a word. The first one has been done for you.

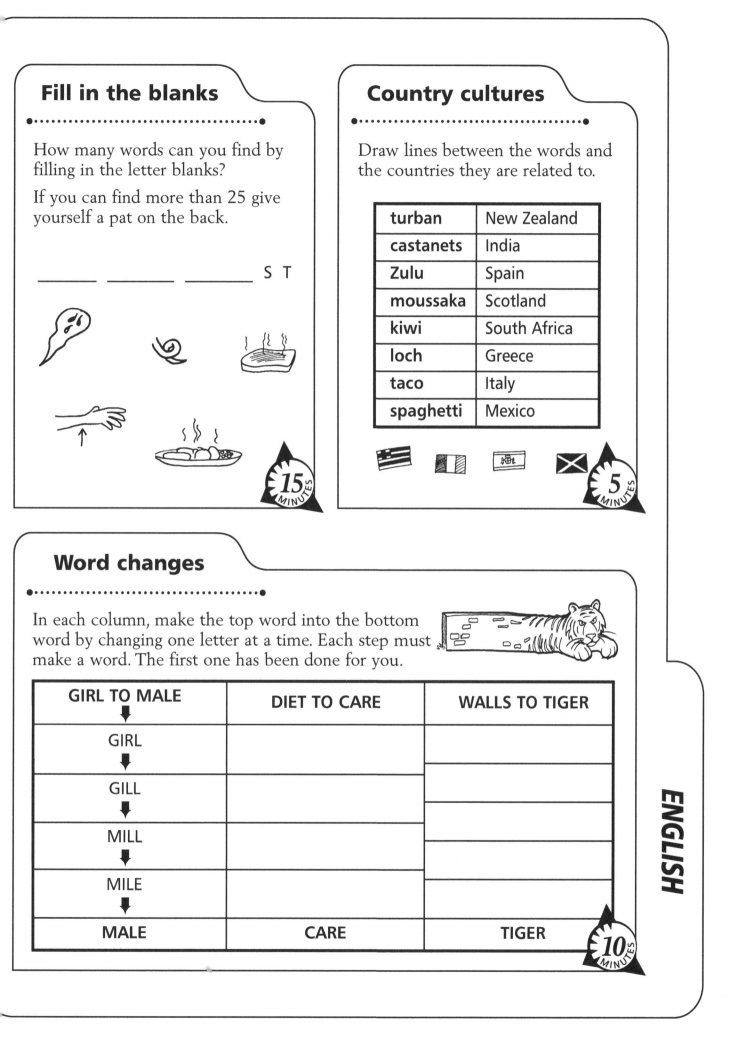

GIRL TO MALE	DIET TO CARE	WALLS TO TIGER
GIRL		
GILL		
MILL		
MILE		
MALE	CARE	TIGER

Brilliant Publications

This page may be reproduced by the original purchaser for non-commercial classroom use.

Timely Tasks for Fast Finishers 9–11 Year Olds

© Blake Publishing

15

ENGLISH

Mix 'n' match

Find the first half of the word that matches the second half to make ten words that fit the clues.

1st half	2nd half	Clue	Answer
wal	nip	vegetable	
twe	hon	large snake	
tur	ble	type of nut	
sta	ond	container for paper money	
pyt	let	pullover	
jum	ana	dry barren land	
mar	ert	number	
des	lve	hard rock	
ban	ble	home of a horse	
alm	per	fruit	

10 MINUTES

Spell well

Exactly half of the words in this list are spelled correctly. Circle them.

brocolli, neice, margerine, anchor, envelope,

assistant, portible, fourwards, accidant, general,

swiming, already, plumer, leopard, libary,

beautifull, evry, written, frown, hedghog, beret,

confectionary, soldier, allways, answer, lizard, easily,

truely, robust, cemetery, addmission, acomodation,

theif, danger, careful, friend.

shed ? wish tap chilp
shamp fap ?

5 MINUTES

Brilliant Publications
This page may be reproduced by the original purchaser for non-commercial classroom use.

Timely Tasks for Fast Finishers 9–11 Year Olds
© Blake Publishing

ENGLISH

Blankety blanks

How many words can you make by filling in the letter blanks?

C __ __ __ E

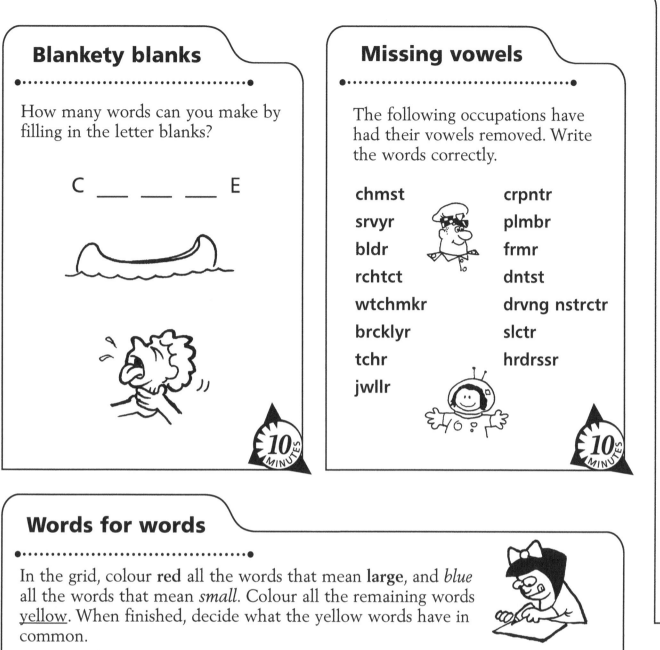

Missing vowels

The following occupations have had their vowels removed. Write the words correctly.

chmst   crpntr
srvyr   plmbr
bldr   frmr
rchtct   dntst
wtchmkr   drvng nstrctr
brcklyr   slctr
tchr   hrdrssr
jwllr

Words for words

In the grid, colour **red** all the words that mean **large**, and *blue* all the words that mean *small*. Colour all the remaining words <u>yellow</u>. When finished, decide what the yellow words have in common.

bellowed	gargantuan	wee	meagre
extensive	puny	enquired	monstrous
argued	groaned	huge	minute
shrunken	gigantic	dwarfish	slight
grumbled	recited	declared	massive
vast	shrivelled	mammoth	colossal
replied	complained	trivial	tiny
stunted	spacious	stammered	giant

ENGLISH

Brilliant Publications

This page may be reproduced by the original purchaser for non-commercial classroom use.

Timely Tasks for Fast Finishers 9–11 Year Olds
© Blake Publishing

17

Origins

Use a dictionary that gives word origins to find out where these words came from and what they mean.

toucan

?

chocolate

gazette

?

spaghetti

yacht

curry

?

dandelion

anthology

?

10 MINUTES

Body parts

Can you write the names of ten parts of your body that have only three letters in them?

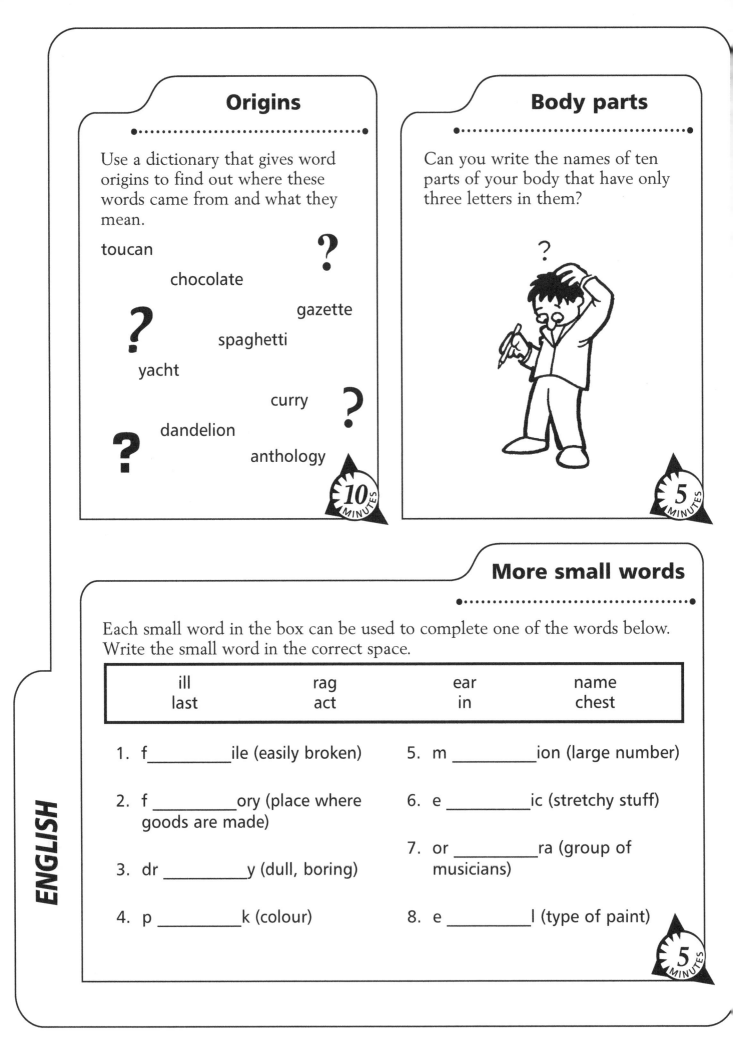

?

5 MINUTES

More small words

Each small word in the box can be used to complete one of the words below. Write the small word in the correct space.

ill	rag	ear	name
last	act	in	chest

1. f_____ile (easily broken)

2. f_____ory (place where goods are made)

3. dr_____y (dull, boring)

4. p_____k (colour)

5. m _____ion (large number)

6. e _____ic (stretchy stuff)

7. or _____ra (group of musicians)

8. e _____l (type of paint)

5 MINUTES

ENGLISH

Brilliant Publications

Timely Tasks for Fast Finishers 9–11 Year Olds

Bull's-eye

What are the ways to score exactly 100 on this dart board?

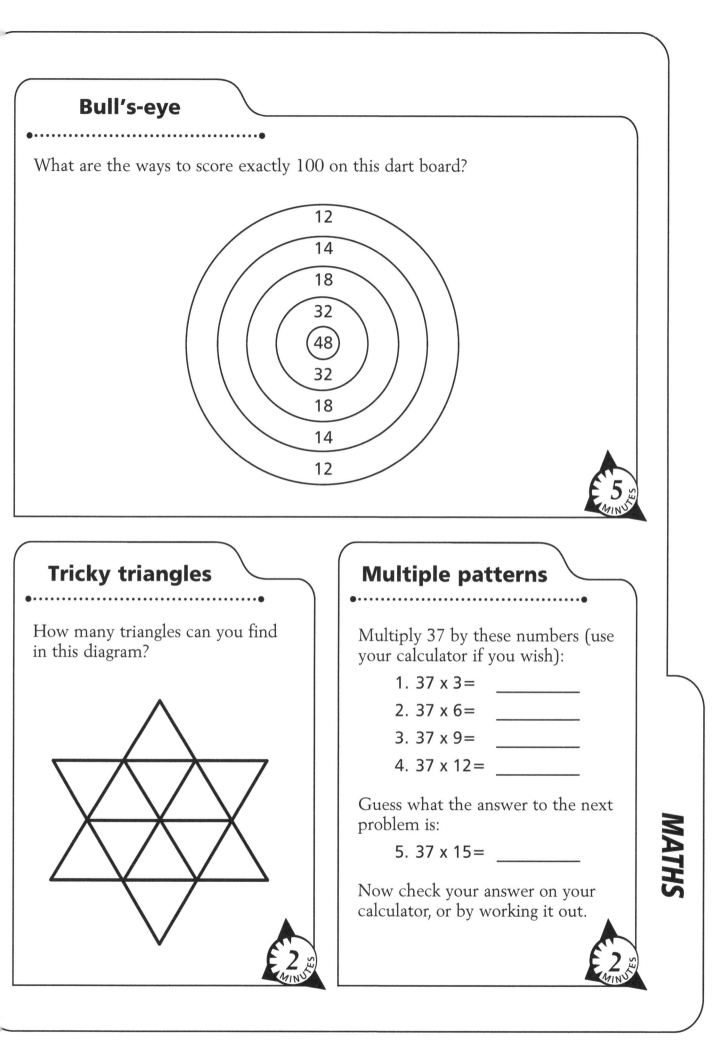

12
14
18
32
(48)
32
18
14
12

5 MINUTES

Tricky triangles

How many triangles can you find in this diagram?

2 MINUTES

Multiple patterns

Multiply 37 by these numbers (use your calculator if you wish):

1. 37 x 3 = _____

2. 37 x 6 = _____

3. 37 x 9 = _____

4. 37 x 12 = _____

Guess what the answer to the next problem is:

5. 37 x 15 = _____

Now check your answer on your calculator, or by working it out.

2 MINUTES

MATHS

Brilliant Publications

This page may be reproduced by the original purchaser for non-commercial classroom use.

Timely Tasks for Fast Finishers 9–11 Year Olds
© Blake Publishing

19

Squared up

Cross out eight lines to leave only two squares.

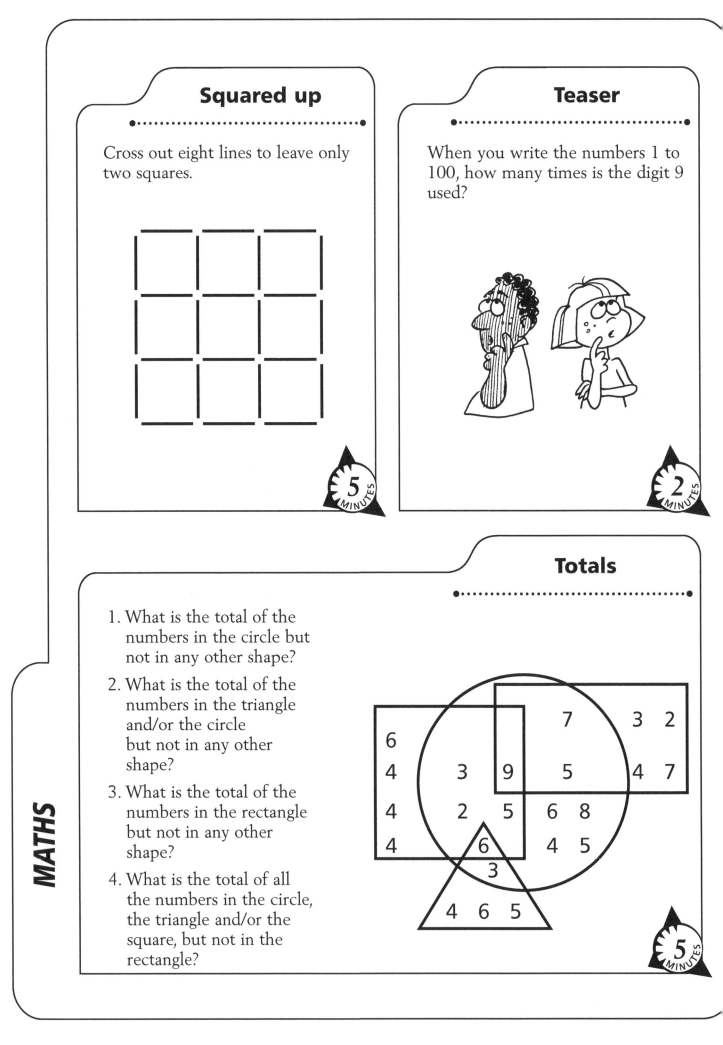

5 MINUTES

Teaser

When you write the numbers 1 to 100, how many times is the digit 9 used?

2 MINUTES

MATHS

Totals

1. What is the total of the numbers in the circle but not in any other shape?

2. What is the total of the numbers in the triangle and/or the circle but not in any other shape?

3. What is the total of the numbers in the rectangle but not in any other shape?

4. What is the total of all the numbers in the circle, the triangle and/or the square, but not in the rectangle?

5 MINUTES

Brilliant Publications

Timely Tasks for Fast Finishers 9–11 Year Olds

© Blake Publishing

Symmetry

Complete the other side of these pictures so that they are symmetrical:

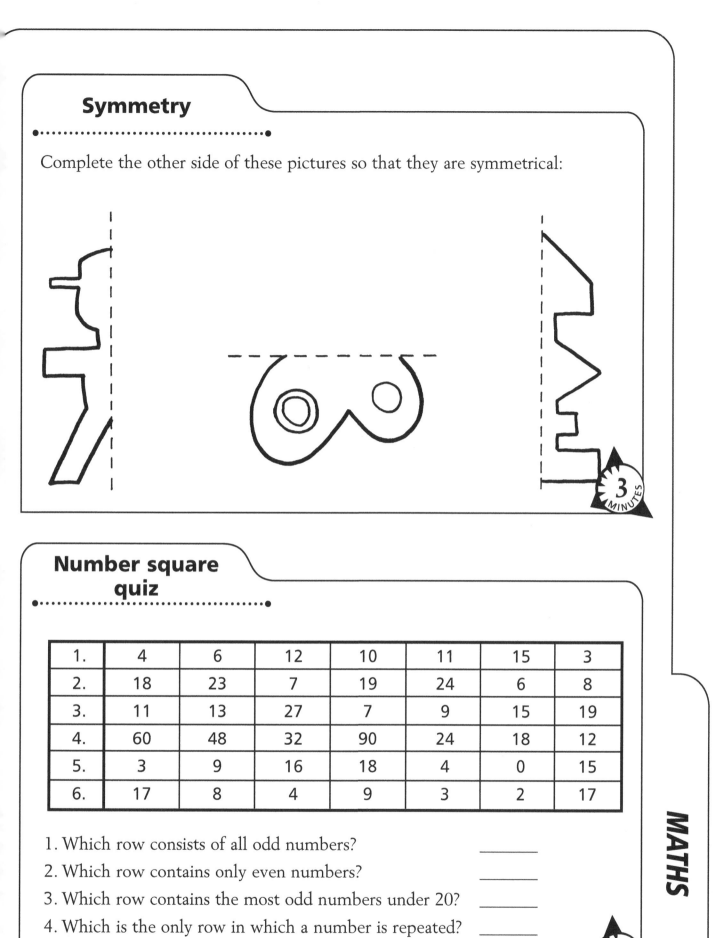

Number square quiz

1.	4	6	12	10	11	15	3
2.	18	23	7	19	24	6	8
3.	11	13	27	7	9	15	19
4.	60	48	32	90	24	18	12
5.	3	9	16	18	4	0	15
6.	17	8	4	9	3	2	17

1. Which row consists of all odd numbers? _____
2. Which row contains only even numbers? _____
3. Which row contains the most odd numbers under 20? _____
4. Which is the only row in which a number is repeated? _____
5. In which row do all the numbers add up to 105? _____

MATHS

Number facts

Study the row of numbers:

11   12   13   14   15   16   17   18   19   20   21   22   23

1. What is the fifth odd number reading from left to right? _____

2. Write down the number exactly halfway between 17 and 23. _____

3. What is the total of the first three even numbers reading from left to right? _____

4. Add together every third number from left to right. _____

5 MINUTES

Line divisions

Draw three lines in this box to make a rectangle and three triangles. The shapes must not overlap. (There is more than one solution.)

3 MINUTES

MATHS

Brilliant Publications

Timely Tasks for Fast Finishers 9–11 Year Olds

© Blake Publishing

Quick think

You have five minutes to solve the following quick sums:

1. Double 12¼ _____
2. Take 6 from 101 _____
3. 16 + 12 + 9 = _____
4. Minutes in 2¼ hours _____
5. Double 14.5 _____
6. Sum of 96 and 86 _____
7. Pence in £19.56 _____
8. Difference between 500 and 156 _____
9. Halve 108½ _____
10. 12 x 10 = 200 – ☐ _____
11. Months in 6¼ years _____
12. Total days in June, July and August _____

Number diamonds

Place a number from 1 to 8 in the circles so that each diamond adds up to 18. You can use each number only once.

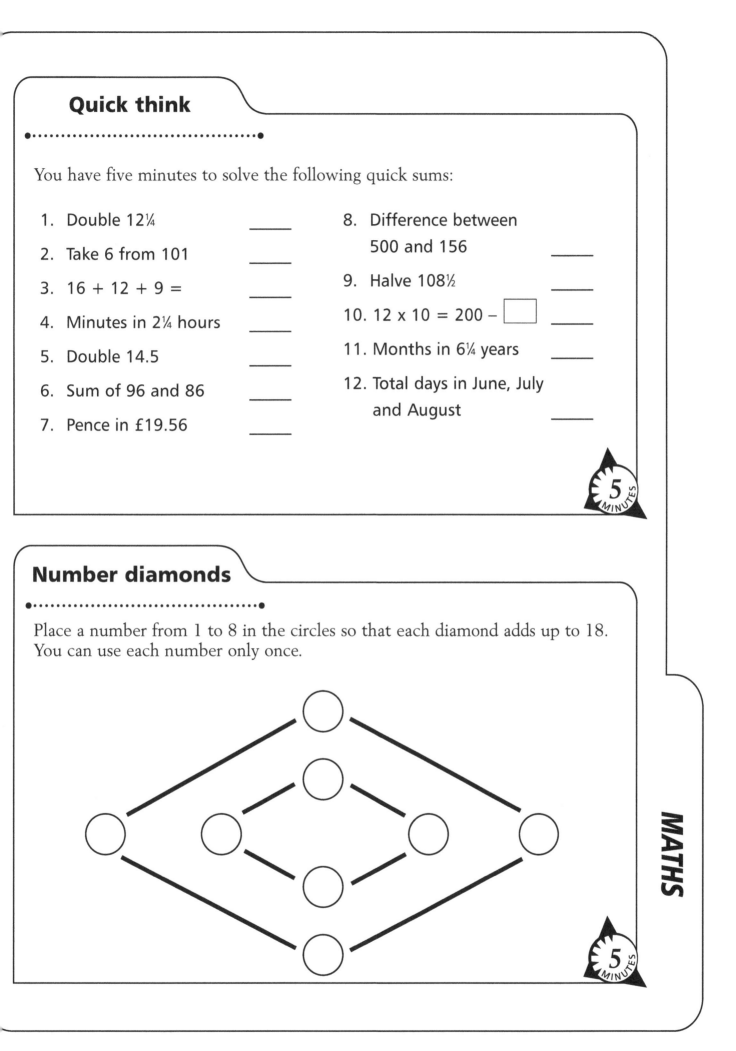

MATHS

Sale time

A supermarket had a sale in which the goods were priced according to the letters in their names:

- 50p for each vowel
- 15p for each consonant

How much did each of the following cost?

1. flour   _____

2. bread   _____

3. margarine   _____

4. detergent   _____

5. sausages   _____

6. butter   _____

5 MINUTES

Target practice

Look at this target. What number do you think is missing from the bull's-eye?

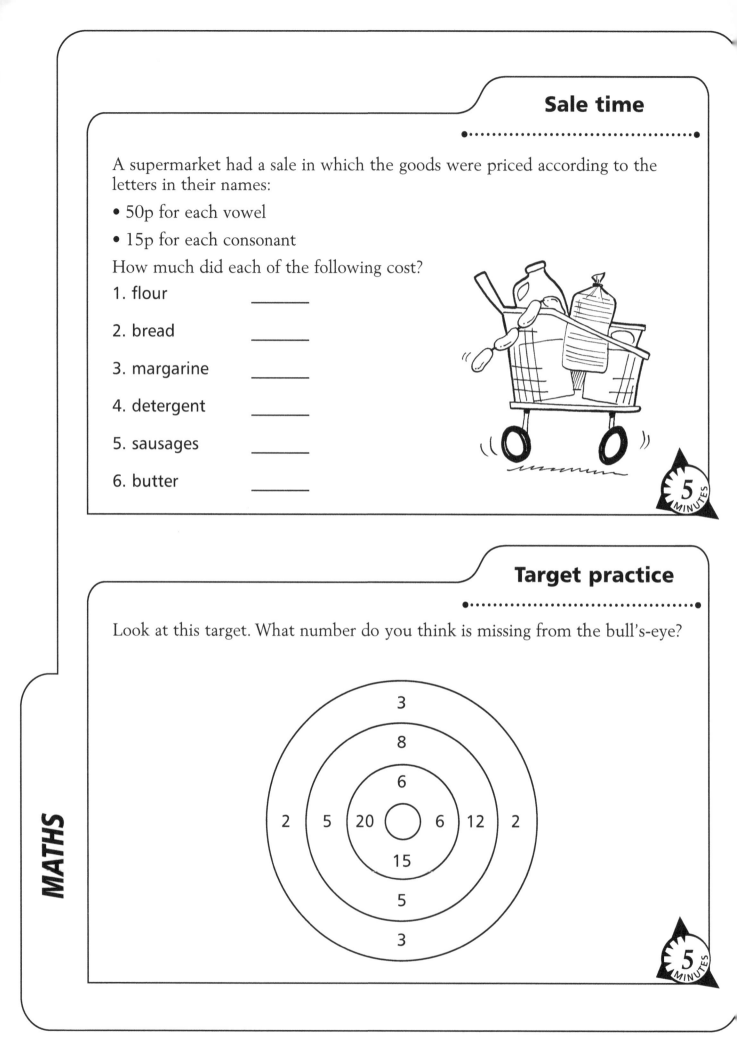

3

8

6

2   5   20   6   12   2

15

5

3

5 MINUTES

MATHS

24

Brilliant Publications

This page may be reproduced by the original purchaser for non-commercial classroom use.

Timely Tasks for Fast Finishers 9–11 Year Olds

Magic squares

Add the missing numbers so the numbers in each square add up to 12 – across, down and diagonally. You can use a number more than once.

7		1
		5

Stop and think

Traffic lights are arranged with red on top, amber in the middle and green at the bottom.

How many other ways could these three colours be arranged?

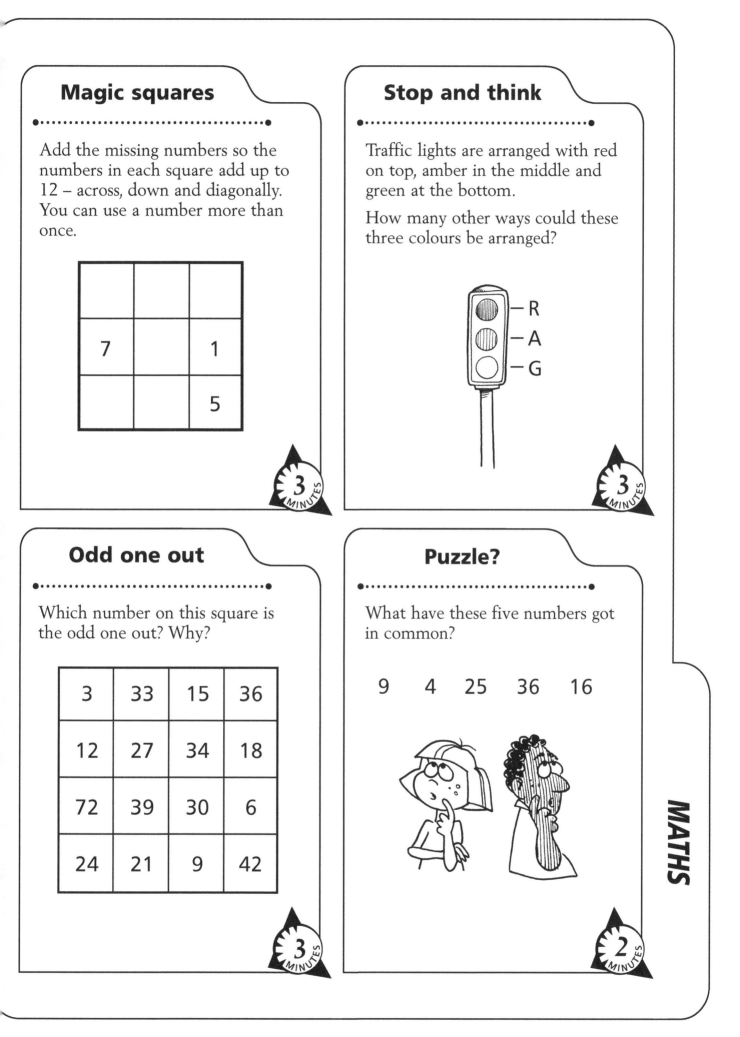

R
A
G

Odd one out

Which number on this square is the odd one out? Why?

3	33	15	36
12	27	34	18
72	39	30	6
24	21	9	42

Puzzle?

What have these five numbers got in common?

9   4   25   36   16

MATHS

Brilliant Publications

This page may be reproduced by the original purchaser for non-commercial classroom use.

Timely Tasks for Fast Finishers 9–11 Year Olds
© Blake Publishing

25

Number quiz

Study the series of numbers, then answer the questions that follow.

a. 2,546
b. 6,804
c. 8,950
d. 5,678

e. 1,654
f. 10,674
g. 4,821

1. Which is the largest of the numbers? _____
2. Which is the smallest of the numbers? _____
3. If you added the digits, what number would add up to 26? _____
4. If you multiplied all the digits, what number would equal 240? _____
5. Which number is not divisible by 2? _____
6. Which number is divisible by both 10 and 5? _____
7. What is the difference between the largest and the smallest number? _____
8. What is the total if you add numbers b, c and d? _____

Clocking it up

Look at each clockface on the left. On the blank clockface beside each one, draw the time which is given.

3¼ hours
later

5¼ hours
later

3 hours 42
mins later

3¼ hours
earlier

6 hours 10
mins earlier

7¼ hours
earlier

MATHS

26

Brilliant Publications

This page may be reproduced by the original purchaser for non-commercial classroom use.

Timely Tasks for Fast Finishers 9–11 Year Olds

© Blake Publishing

Colour squares

Work out the answer to the problems below, then colour the square containing the answer in the correct colour.

Colour	Question	Answer
Red	$8 + 12 + 9 + 7$	
Light Blue	$5^2 + 4^2$	
Green	Prime numbers between 12 and 20	
Pink	$(96 \div 2) - (16 \div 4)$	
Yellow	$70 - 15 - 54$	
Brown	$100 - 26 - 34$	
Dark Blue	$4 \times 8 + 28 - 11$	
Black	$(70 \div 5) + 3^2$	

1	2	3	4	5	6	7	8	9	10
11	12	13	14	15	16	17	18	19	20
21	22	23	24	25	26	27	28	29	30
31	32	33	34	35	36	37	38	39	40
41	42	43	44	45	46	47	48	49	50
51	52	53	54	55	56	57	58	59	60
61	62	63	64	65	66	67	68	69	70

5 MINUTES

Magic squares

Add the rows, columns and diagonals of this magic square and write your answers on the lines provided.

What is the special property of this magic square? (Use a calculator to help you.)

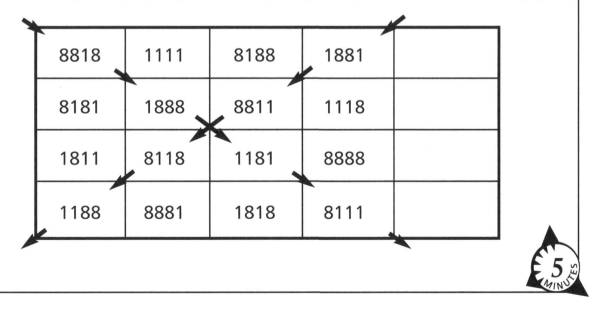

8818	1111	8188	1881	
8181	1888	8811	1118	
1811	8118	1181	8888	
1188	8881	1818	8111	

5 MINUTES

MATHS

Cross tots

Add across and down. If you are correct, your totals will match exactly (i.e. totals across and down) when added.

379	+	743	+	538	+	653	=	_____
468	+	106	+	107	+	244	=	_____
372	+	293	+	300	+	117	=	_____
150	+	174	+	425	+	209	=	_____
+		+		+		=	
___		___		___		___		___

10 MINUTES

Circling round

In each circle, the centre number is the total of some of the numbers around the circle. Colour these numbers.

1.
5	7
5	8
16	**20**	3
5	9

2.
18	30
6	8
4	**35**	10
11	3

3.
3	11
8	8
7	**46**	9
4	12

4.
17	3
4	8
10	**58**	0
11	12

5.
17	15
25	3
15	**75**	11
9	20

6.
25	5
18	60
5	**110**	9
15	12

7.
10	1
12	30
12	**68**	8
15	9

8.
12	45
1	9
25	**124**	12
3	30

15 MINUTES

MATHS

Brilliant Publications
This page may be reproduced by the original purchaser for non-commercial classroom use.

Timely Tasks for Fast Finishers 9–11 Year Olds
© Blake Publishing

Parallel partners

Parallel lines are straight lines that never intersect, like this | |.

Please draw a picture of a table on a rug, using as many sets of parallel lines as possible.

Dropping off

Look at this picture of eight triangles. Remove four lines to leave just four triangles.

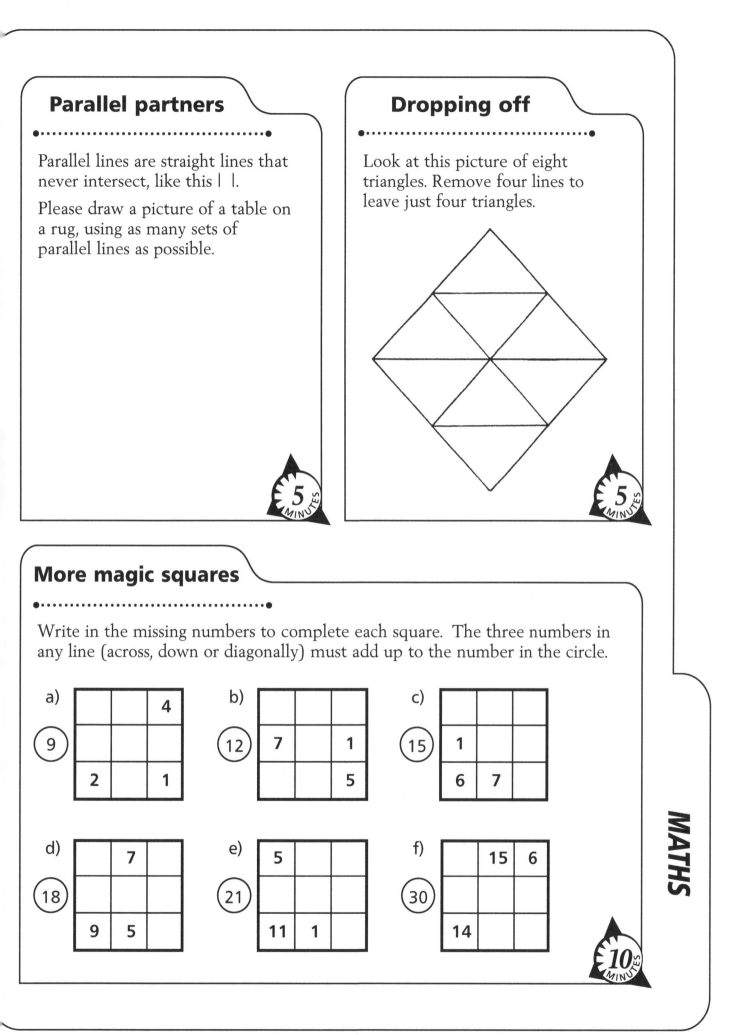

More magic squares

Write in the missing numbers to complete each square. The three numbers in any line (across, down or diagonally) must add up to the number in the circle.

a) 9

		4
2		1

b) 12

7		1
		5

c) 15

1		
	6	7

d) 18

	7	
9	5	

e) 21

5		
	11	1

f) 30

	15	6
14		

MATHS

Brilliant Publications

This page may be reproduced by the original purchaser for non-commercial classroom use.

Timely Tasks for Fast Finishers 9–11 Year Olds

© Blake Publishing

29

Number quiz

All these answers are numbers!

1. How many is a crowd?
2. How many dalmatians?
3. How many leagues under the sea?
4. How many lives for a cat?
5. How many stitches do we save?
6. How many is a baker's dozen?
7. How many blackbirds in the pie?
8. Ali Baba and how many thieves?
9. How many days of Christmas?
10. How many is company?

5 MINUTES

Square pathways

Colour all the squares **red** counting by **7s to 140.**

Colour all the squares *blue* counting by *8s to 144.*

15	7	12	8	16	8	80	74	91
14	4	11	12	24	41	91	83	86
21	16	14	18	32	40	37	107	48
28	35	42	17	61	48	61	53	17
11	17	49	33	38	56	112	119	36
63	56	91	72	64	105	36	144	126
70	18	43	80	98	44	136	128	133
15	77	84	91	88	96	104	120	140
47	86	93	57	60	108	116	112	133

5 MINUTES

Factor fun

Write in the missing factors to complete these factor trees. The first one has been done for you.

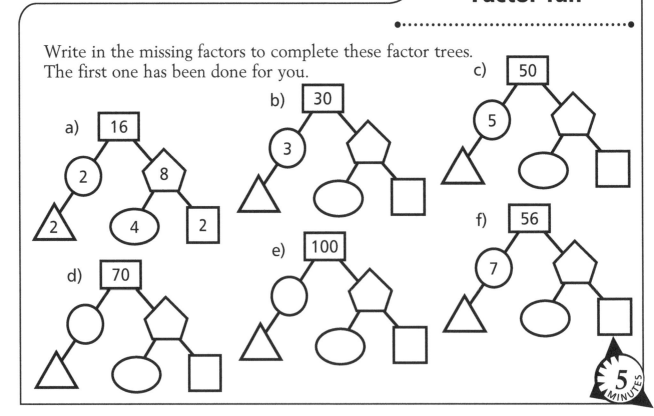

5 MINUTES

Brilliant Publications

Timely Tasks for Fast Finishers 9–11 Year Olds

MATHS

Twenty-one is sharp

Colour in all the pairs of triangles that share a common side and add up to 21.
What sign do the coloured triangles make?

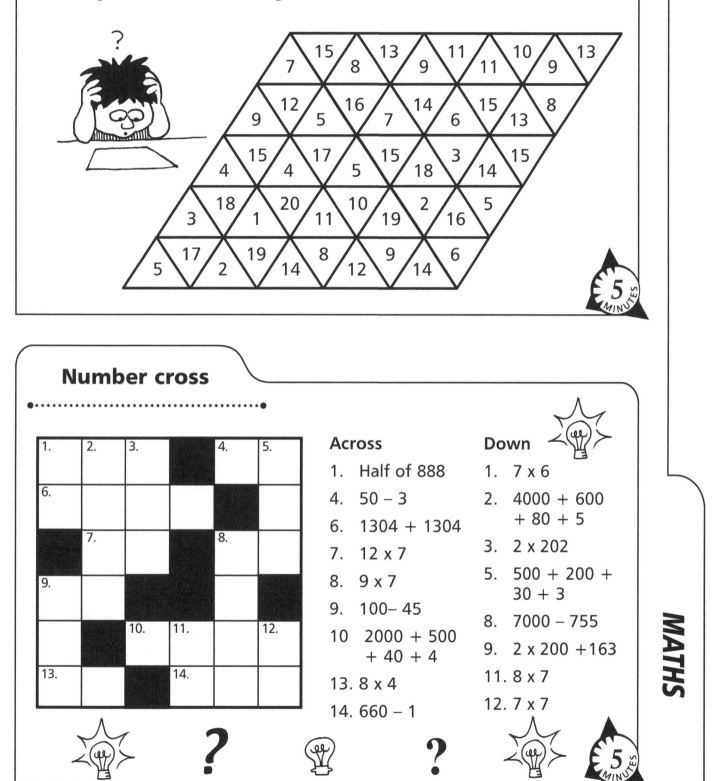

Number cross

1.	2.	3.		4.	5.
6.					
	7.			8.	
9.					
		10.	11.		12.
13.			14.		

Across
1. Half of 888
4. 50 − 3
6. 1304 + 1304
7. 12 x 7
8. 9 x 7
9. 100− 45
10 2000 + 500 + 40 + 4
13. 8 x 4
14. 660 − 1

Down
1. 7 x 6
2. 4000 + 600 + 80 + 5
3. 2 x 202
5. 500 + 200 + 30 + 3
8. 7000 − 755
9. 2 x 200 +163
11. 8 x 7
12. 7 x 7

MATHS

Brilliant Publications

This page may be reproduced by the original purchaser for non-commercial classroom use.

Timely Tasks for Fast Finishers 9–11 Year Olds
© Blake Publishing

31

Boxing on

Colour all the three touching boxes that have a product of 80.

Boxes may be used more than once.

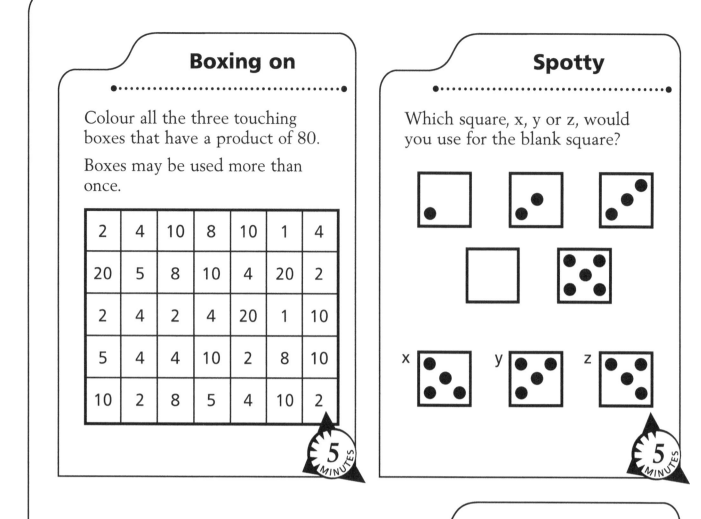

2	4	10	8	10	1	4
20	5	8	10	4	20	2
2	4	2	4	20	1	10
5	4	4	10	2	8	10
10	2	8	5	4	10	2

Spotty

Which square, x, y or z, would you use for the blank square?

x   y   z

What number?

Can you work out what each number is?

1. I am a number between 5 and 15. The sum of my digits is odd. One of the digits is twice the other. _____

2. I am a number between 20 and 50. One digit is half the other. The product of the digits is twice the sum of the digits. _____

3. I am a number over 200 but less than 300. All my digits are even. No two digits are the same. The sum of my digits is 12. _____

4. I am more than 100 but less than 200. I am divisible by 5. The sum and product of my digits are divisible by 5. My three digits are odd. _____

5. I am less than 50 but more than 20. The sum and product of my two digits are the same. _____

MATHS

Signing on

In each problem you have three numbers, an equals sign and a total.

Keep the order of the numbers the same and use +, –, x or ÷ in the boxes to make the three numbers equal the total.

1. 3 ☐ 2 ☐ 4 = 10

2. 8 ☐ 8 ☐ 6 = 10

3. 20 ☐ 5 ☐ 4 = 8

4. 12 ☐ 4 ☐ 2 = 16

5. 14 ☐ 6 ☐ 10 = 30

6. 20 ☐ 4 ☐ 6 = 10

7. 5 ☐ 3 ☐ 5 = 20

8. 30 ☐ 6 ☐ 12 = 17

9. 40 ☐ 20 ☐ 20 = 0

10. 7 ☐ 7 ☐ 2 = 28

10 MINUTES

Shipshapes

Follow the instructions below each shape to make some new shapes.

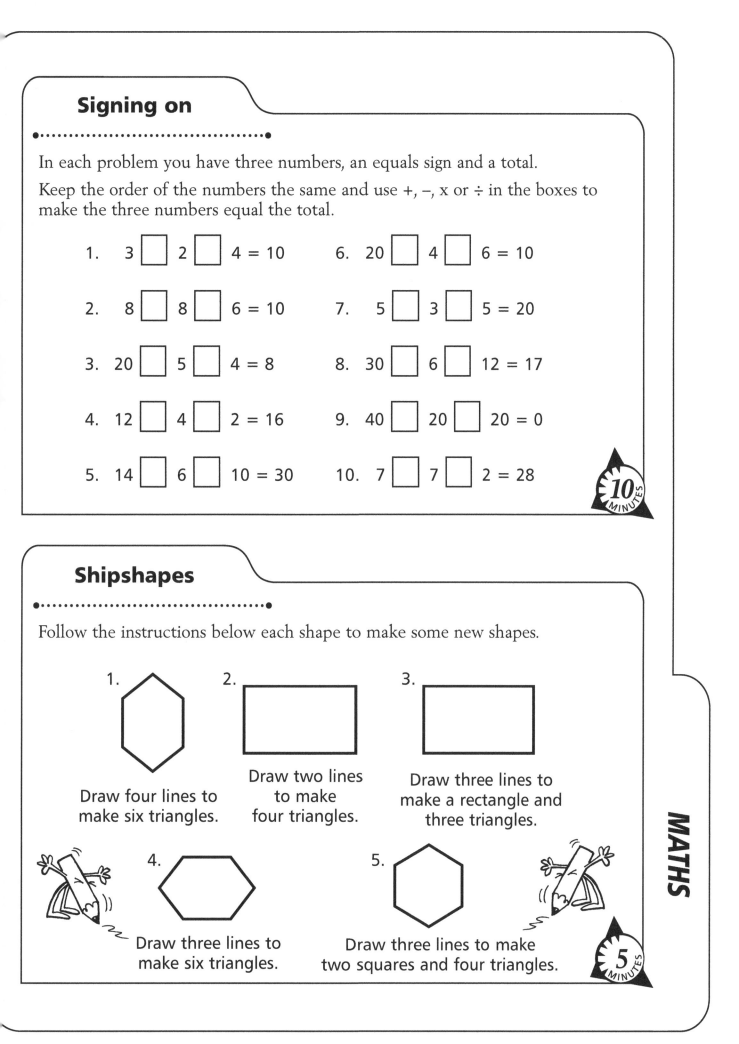

1. Draw four lines to make six triangles.

2. Draw two lines to make four triangles.

3. Draw three lines to make a rectangle and three triangles.

4. Draw three lines to make six triangles.

5. Draw three lines to make two squares and four triangles.

5 MINUTES

MATHS

Brilliant Publications

This page may be reproduced by the original purchaser for non-commercial classroom use.

Timely Tasks for Fast Finishers 9–11 Year Olds

© Blake Publishing

33

What's the end?

Start with the number given at the top of each table. Then follow through each step and write the answers.

1.

Begin with 30	
Double it	
Subtract 10	
Divide by 5	
Add 40	
Multiply by 6	

2.

Begin with 12	
Multiply by 4	
Double it	
Divide it by 4	
Halve it	
Triple it	

3.

Begin with 70	
Double it	
Double it again	
Add 500	
Divide by 3	
Multiply by 10	

4.

Begin with 750	
Double it	
Divide it by 3	
Subtract 250	
Halve it	
Divide by 5	

5 MINUTES

Number words

How well do you know the numbers represented by words?

1. A period of ten years is a _____.
2. A hundred runs in cricket is a _____.
3. A stand with three legs is a _____.
4. A creature with one hundred legs is a _____.
5. A hexagon has _____ sides.
6. A sea creature with eight tentacles is an _____.
7. A song for two people is a _____.
8. Two things the same (e.g., socks) make a _____.
9. A bike with three wheels is a _____.
10. A quintet is a group of _____ musicians.
11. An octogenarian is between the ages of _____ and _____ .
12. A plane with two sets of wings is a _____.

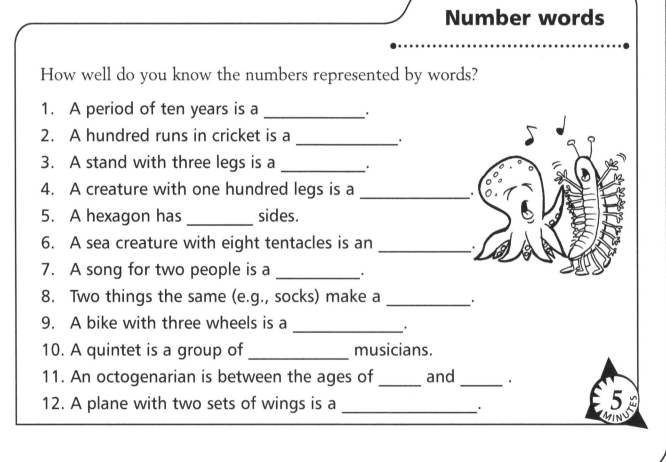

5 MINUTES

Brilliant Publications

This page may be reproduced by the original purchaser for non-commercial classroom use.

Timely Tasks for Fast Finishers 9–11 Year Olds

© Blake Publishing

MATHS

Picture problem

Work out the sums in each square and then draw the picture in the square below that contains the answer. If you do it correctly, the second grid will contain a picture of a common reptile.

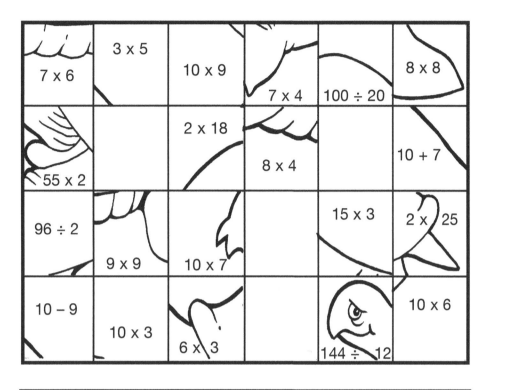

7 x 6	3 x 5	10 x 9	7 x 4	100 ÷ 20	8 x 8
55 x 2		2 x 18	8 x 4		10 + 7
96 ÷ 2	9 x 9	10 x 7		15 x 3	2 x 25
10 – 9	10 x 3	6 x 3		144 ÷ 12	10 x 6

40	25	36	5	1	24
12	18	60	21	17	15
90	110	45	30	48	50
70	28	32	42	81	64

MATHS

Pattern colour

Colour or shade this design to highlight the different shapes and patterns.

Use different colours or different shades of pencil from dark to light.

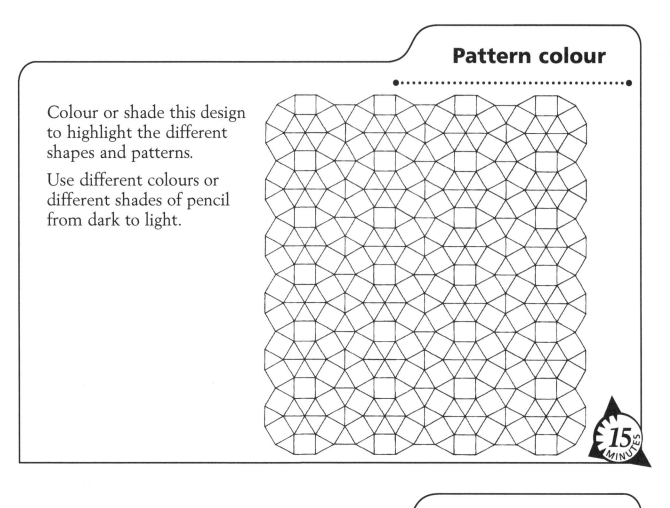

Careful colouring

Colouring a map takes careful planning. Using only four different colours, colour the outlined areas so that each one is a different colour from all the ones touching it.

THINKING

Brilliant Publications

This page may be reproduced by the original purchaser for non-commercial classroom use.

Timely Tasks for Fast Finishers 9–11 Year Olds

© Blake Publishing

Colour or shade the object below to design your own optical illusion. There's no right or wrong way to do it.

Use either different colours to highlight optical aspects, or different shades of pencil, from light to dark.

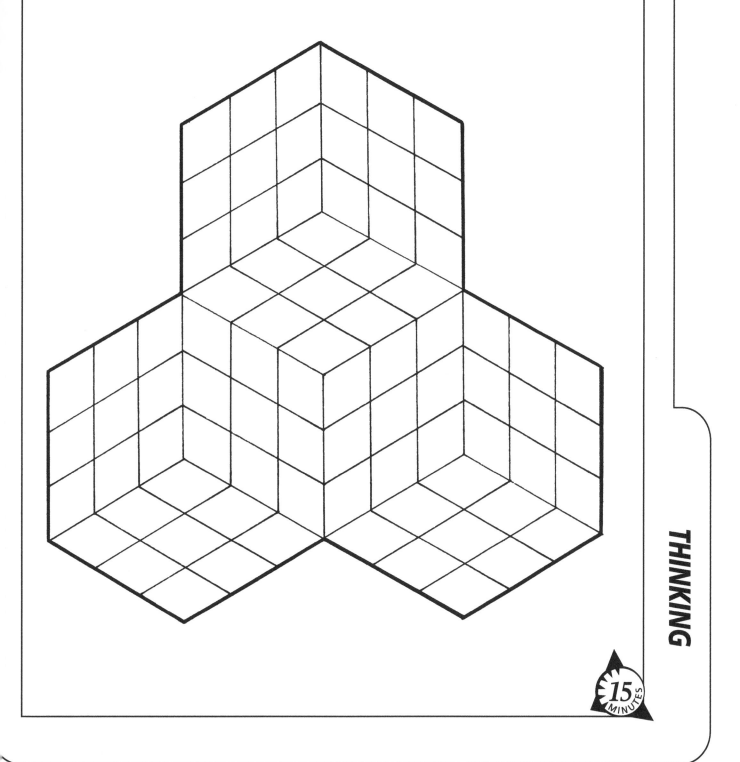

THINKING

Brilliant Publications

This page may be reproduced by the original purchaser for non-commercial classroom use.

Timely Tasks for Fast Finishers 9–11 Year Olds

© Blake Publishing

37

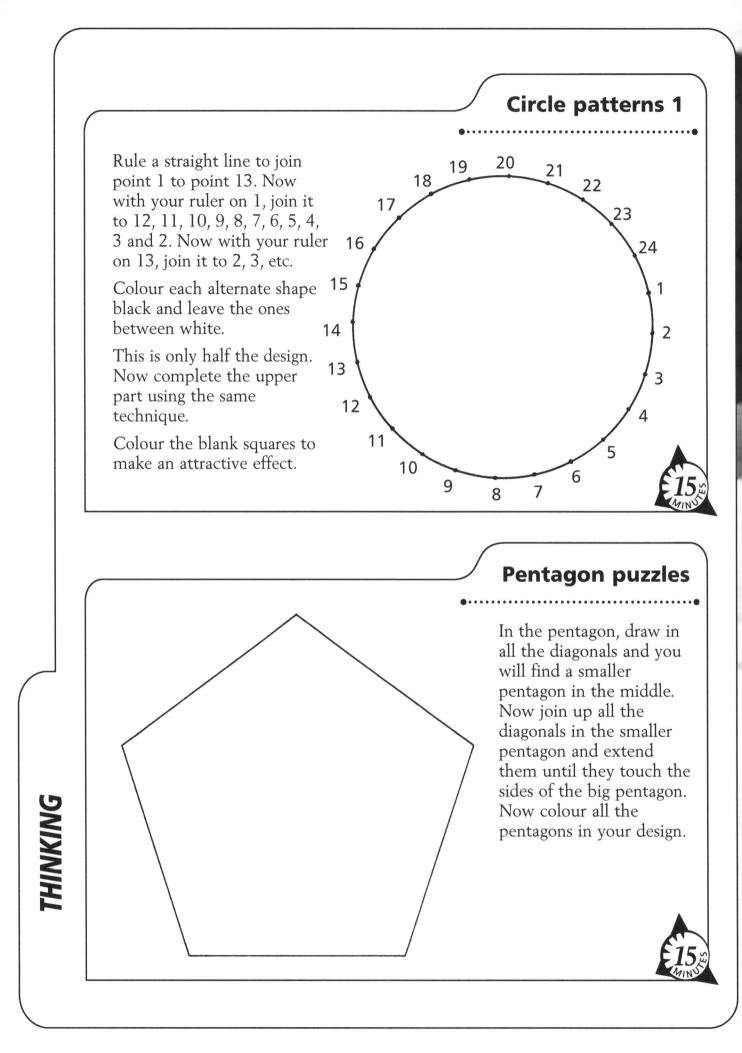

Circle patterns 1

Rule a straight line to join point 1 to point 13. Now with your ruler on 1, join it to 12, 11, 10, 9, 8, 7, 6, 5, 4, 3 and 2. Now with your ruler on 13, join it to 2, 3, etc.

Colour each alternate shape black and leave the ones between white.

This is only half the design. Now complete the upper part using the same technique.

Colour the blank squares to make an attractive effect.

Pentagon puzzles

In the pentagon, draw in all the diagonals and you will find a smaller pentagon in the middle. Now join up all the diagonals in the smaller pentagon and extend them until they touch the sides of the big pentagon. Now colour all the pentagons in your design.

THINKING

Brilliant Publications

Timely Tasks for Fast Finishers 9–11 Year Olds

Wood grain

Using a sharp lead pencil or a black pen, draw lines down the page and around the spots to create a wood-grain effect. Keep the lines you draw close to each other. When you have finished colour your pattern in tones and shades of timber.

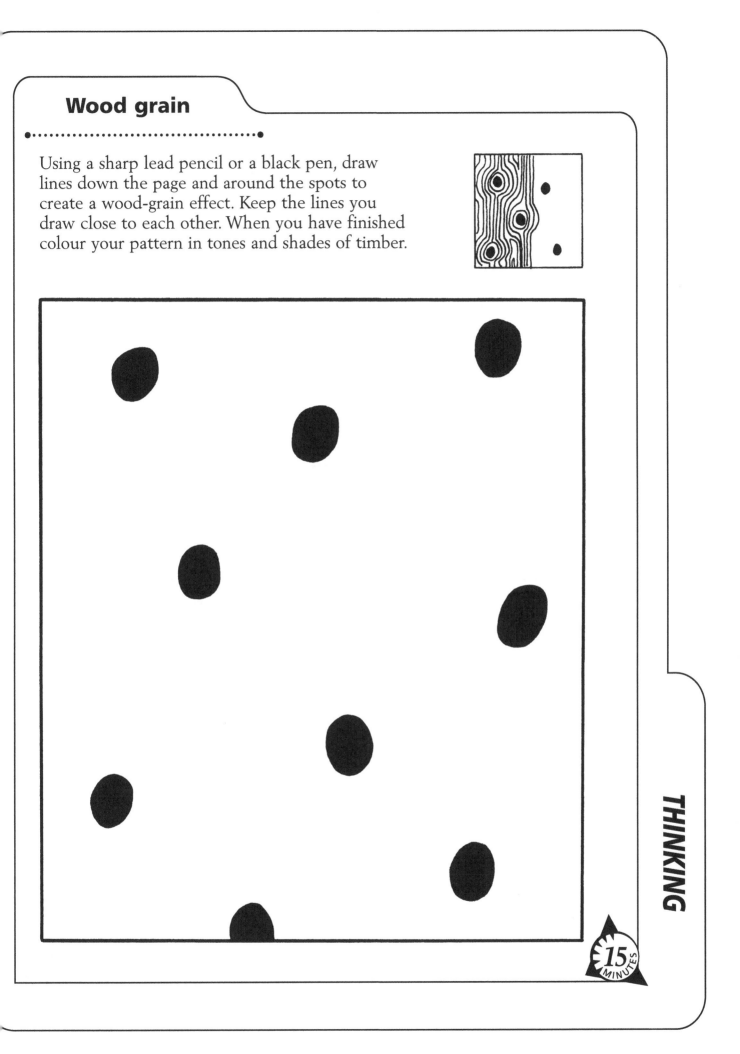

THINKING

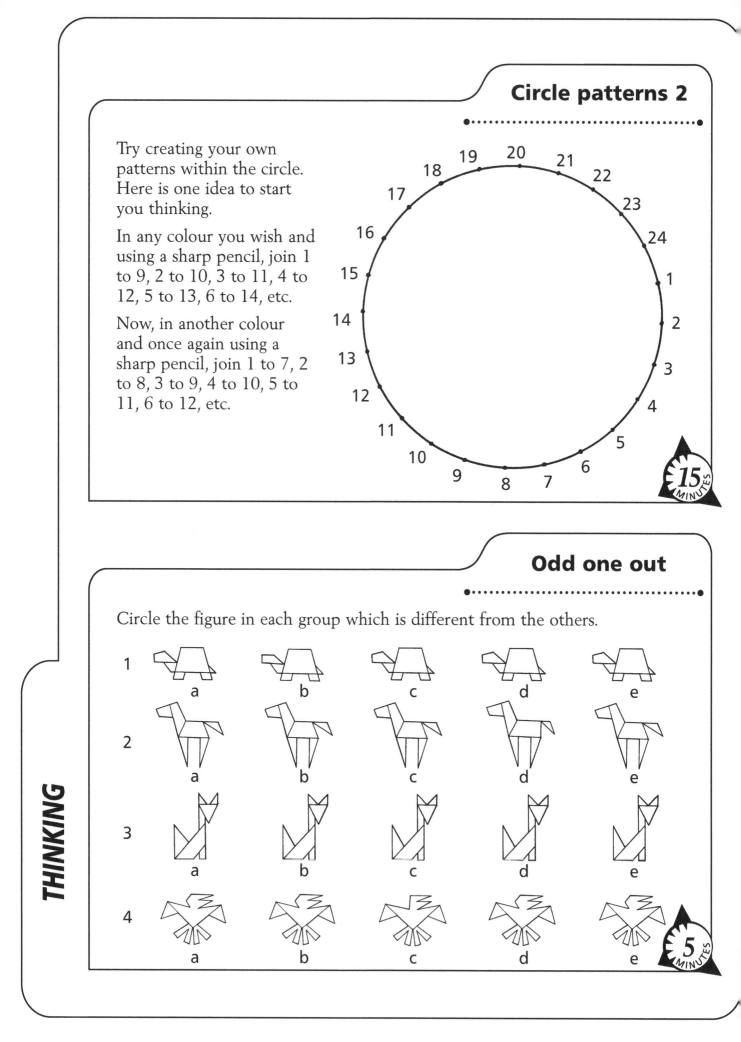

Circle patterns 2

Try creating your own patterns within the circle. Here is one idea to start you thinking.

In any colour you wish and using a sharp pencil, join 1 to 9, 2 to 10, 3 to 11, 4 to 12, 5 to 13, 6 to 14, etc.

Now, in another colour and once again using a sharp pencil, join 1 to 7, 2 to 8, 3 to 9, 4 to 10, 5 to 11, 6 to 12, etc.

15 MINUTES

Odd one out

Circle the figure in each group which is different from the others.

1   a   b   c   d   e

2   a   b   c   d   e

3   a   b   c   d   e

4   a   b   c   d   e

5 MINUTES

THINKING

Brilliant Publications

Timely Tasks for Fast Finishers 9–11 Year Olds

© Blake Publishing

Tantalizing tiles

Connect the dots in the box below to make this pattern. Then colour it as you wish.

THINKING

20 MINUTES

Picture sayings

Sometimes we are able to represent well-known sayings or expressions by illustrating them. Work out the following.

For example:  = hot under the collar.

1. STAND
   I
   _____

2. OVER
   _____

3. _____

4. _____

Memory test

Study the objects below for two minutes. When time is up, cover them and write down as many as you can remember.

THINKING

Brilliant Publications
This page may be reproduced by the original purchaser for non-commercial classroom use.

Timely Tasks for Fast Finishers 9–11 Year Olds
© Blake Publishing

Classifying creatures

Gerakaffs, trituffs and zonuffs are creatures that live on the planet of Jopitus. On your first visit to this planet, a local inhabitant tells you how to distinguish which creature is which:

- A gerakaff is any creature with at least two eyes.
- A trituff is any gerakaff with a triangular hump on its back.
- A zonuff is any creature with a triangular hump on its back that is not a gerakaff.

a. _____

1. Identify each creature and write above it what it is.

b. _____

2. Draw a gerakaff that is not a trituff.

c. _____

3. Draw a trituff that is not a gerakaff.

THINKING

5 MINUTES

Brilliant Publications

This page may be reproduced by the original purchaser for non-commercial classroom use.

Timely Tasks for Fast Finishers 9–11 Year Olds

© Blake Publishing

43

Make a letter

Nine of these 12 boxes can be used to form a capital letter. Try at first to identify the letter using your eyes only, then cut out the squares and put them together in the correct order to make the letter.

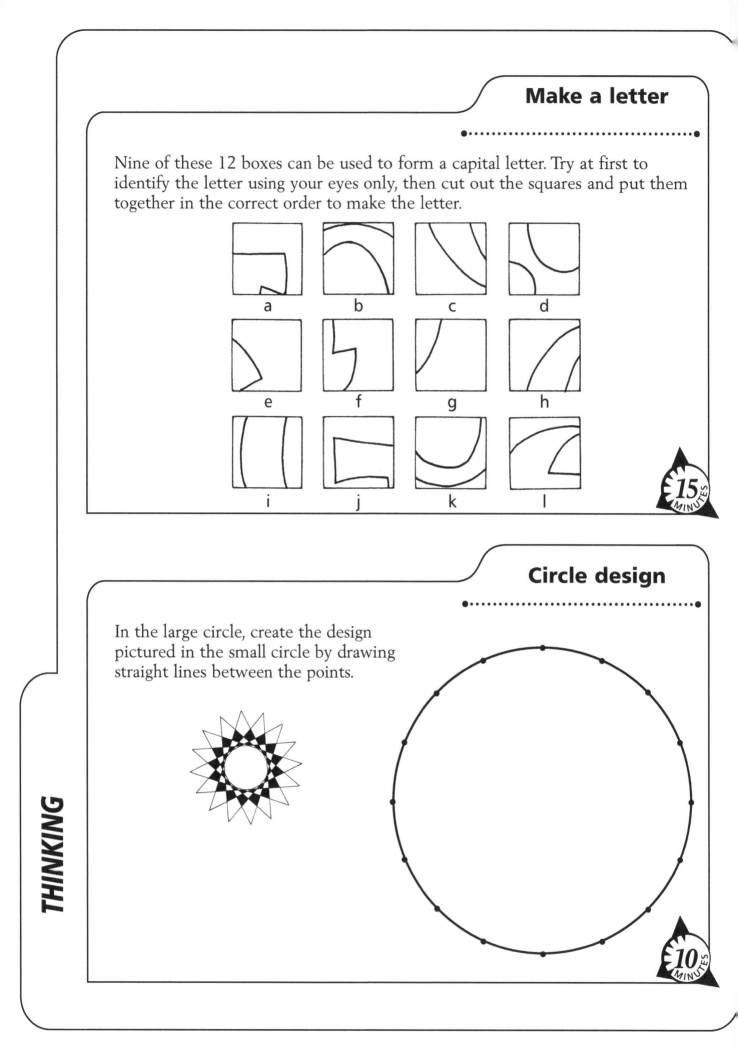

a   b   c   d

e   f   g   h

i   j   k   l

15 MINUTES

Circle design

In the large circle, create the design pictured in the small circle by drawing straight lines between the points.

10 MINUTES

THINKING

44

Brilliant Publications
This page may be reproduced by the original purchaser for non-commercial classroom use.

Timely Tasks for Fast Finishers 9–11 Year Olds
© Blake Publishing

Viewing

Look closely at the mythical creature below. In each box, draw what you think it would look like from the position listed.

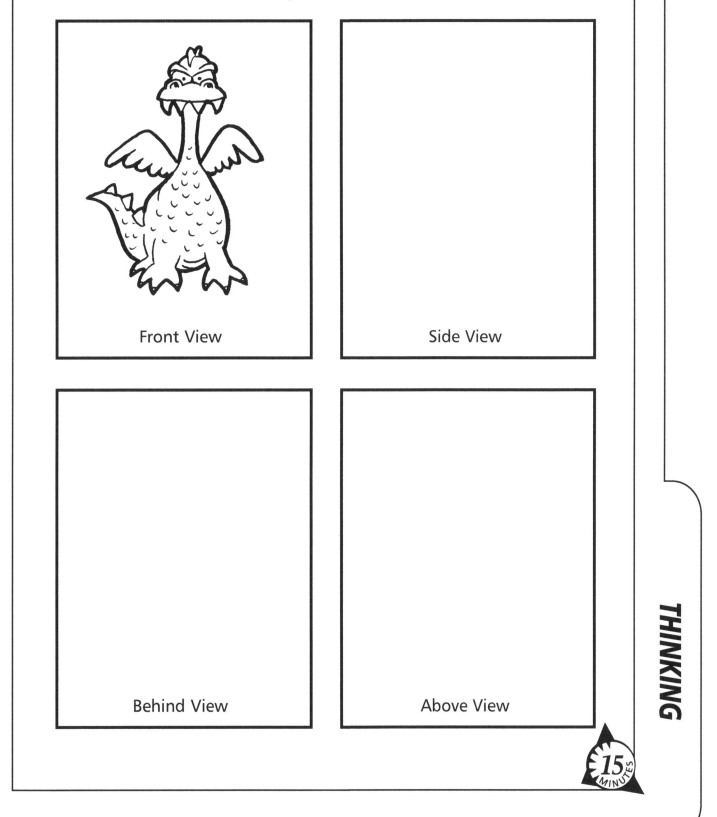

Front View

Side View

Behind View

Above View

Brilliant Publications

This page may be reproduced by the original purchaser for non-commercial classroom use.

Timely Tasks for Fast Finishers 9–11 Year Olds
© Blake Publishing

45

The following octagons may look identical at first, but actually they can be divided into four identical pairs. Draw lines to join the identical pairs.

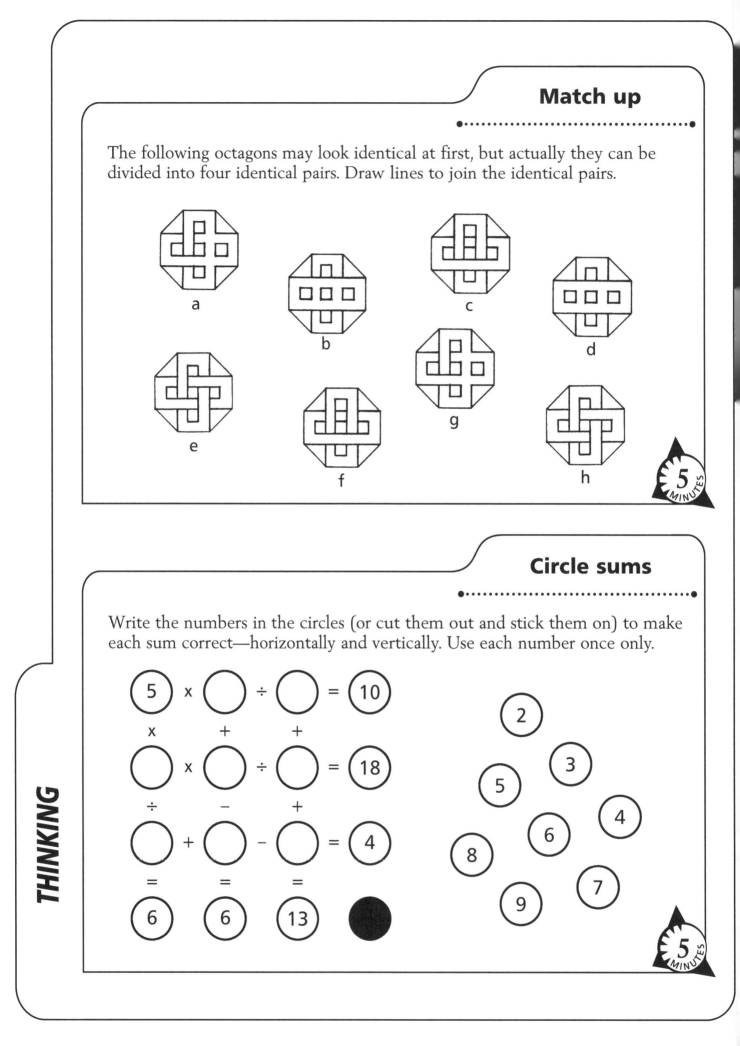

Circle sums

Write the numbers in the circles (or cut them out and stick them on) to make each sum correct—horizontally and vertically. Use each number once only.

THINKING

46

Brilliant Publications
This page may be reproduced by the original purchaser for non-commercial classroom use.

Timely Tasks for Fast Finishers 9–11 Year Olds
© Blake Publishing

Eye challenges

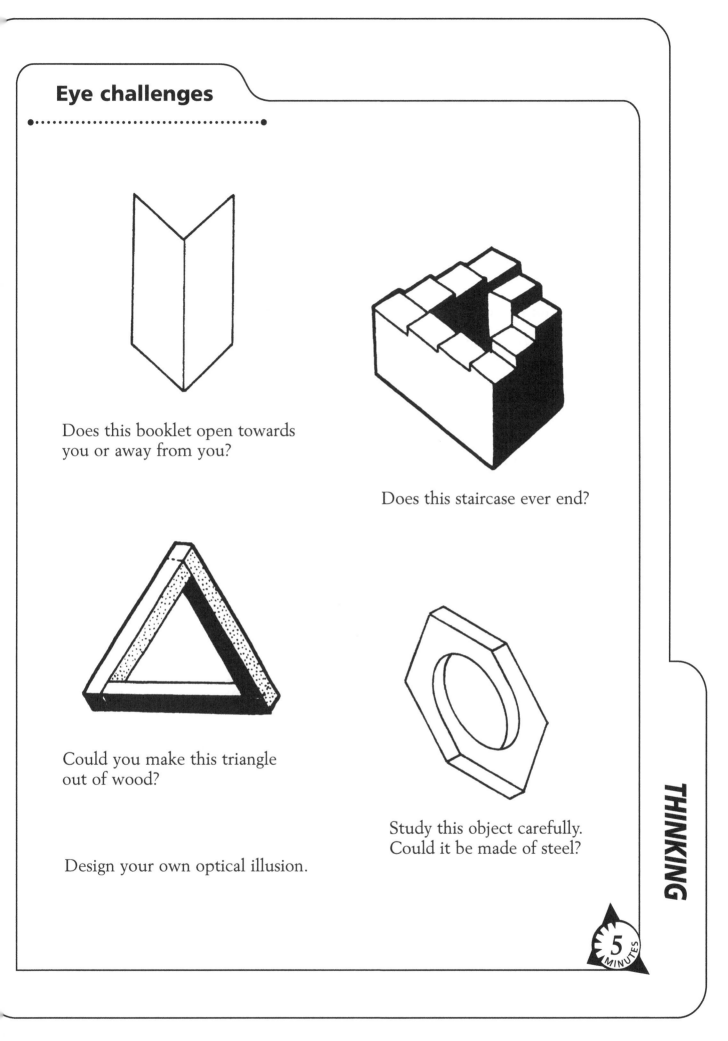

Does this booklet open towards you or away from you?

Does this staircase ever end?

Could you make this triangle out of wood?

Design your own optical illusion.

Study this object carefully. Could it be made of steel?

5 MINUTES

• •

The following questions are not hard as long as you are prepared to think a little!

1. A farmer had 27 ducks and all but 11 died. How many ducks are left?

2. What continents are south of the North Pole?

3. Write this number as quickly as you can! *Eleven thousand, one hundred and eleven.*

4. What letter comes next in this pattern? A C E G I __

5. How many of our months have 28 days?

6. How much soil can be removed from a hole that is exactly one metre deep, one metre wide and one metre long?

7. A post outside a hotel in the Wild West of America had the following sign attached to it. Can you explain what the post was used for?

```
T O T I
E M U L
E S T O
```

(15 MINUTES)

Who?

• •

Question your classmates to find the information you need. Write your answers on a separate sheet and make a graph from them.

How many classmates:

... have a birthday in the same month as you?	... can wiggle their ears?	... have brown eyes?	... know the seven colours of the rainbow?
... wear the same size shoes as you?	... dislike cats?	... dislike pizza?	... love reading?
... were not in the same class as you last year?	... have more than three brothers and/or sisters?	... are an Aries or a Pisces?	... have the same given name as you?
... have been overseas for a holiday?	... ride a bicycle to school?	... like eating celery?	... can say the 7 times table in under 20 seconds?

(20 MINUTES)

THINKING

48 Brilliant Publications
This page may be reproduced by the original purchaser for non-commercial classroom use.

Timely Tasks for Fast Finishers 9–11 Year Olds
© Blake Publishing

Our environment —1

Imagine some oil was spilled in the pond and all the mosquito larvae died. Describe the effect it may have on the other creatures in the picture. Explain why.

The effect on other creatures

_____

_____

_____

_____

_____

_____

SCIENCE

Look at the picture below. Describe how the environment is being affected and what could be done to improve it.

How the environment is being affected

_____

_____

_____

_____

_____

_____

_____

What can be done to improve it

_____

_____

_____

_____

_____

_____

_____

SCIENCE

50

Brilliant Publications

This page may be reproduced by the original purchaser for non-commercial classroom use.

Timely Tasks for Fast Finishers 9–11 Year Olds

© Blake Publishing

Our bodies

In what parts of the body are the following bones found?

rib _____   humerus _____

radius _____   ulna _____

patella _____   tarsus _____

carpus _____   fibula _____

tibia _____   stapes _____

clavicle _____   femur _____

skull _____   metatarsal _____

5 MINUTES

Energy

Look carefully at this list of people:
- farmer
- elderly person ill in hospital
- taxi driver
- doctor
- teacher

- footballer in training for the coming season
- coal miner
- person confined to a wheelchair

Choose the one who would require the most daily energy and say why this is so.

_____

_____

Now choose the one who would require the least daily energy and say why.

_____

_____

10 MINUTES

SCIENCE

Brilliant Publications
This page may be reproduced by the original purchaser for non-commercial classroom use.

Timely Tasks for Fast Finishers 9–11 Year Olds
© Blake Publishing

51

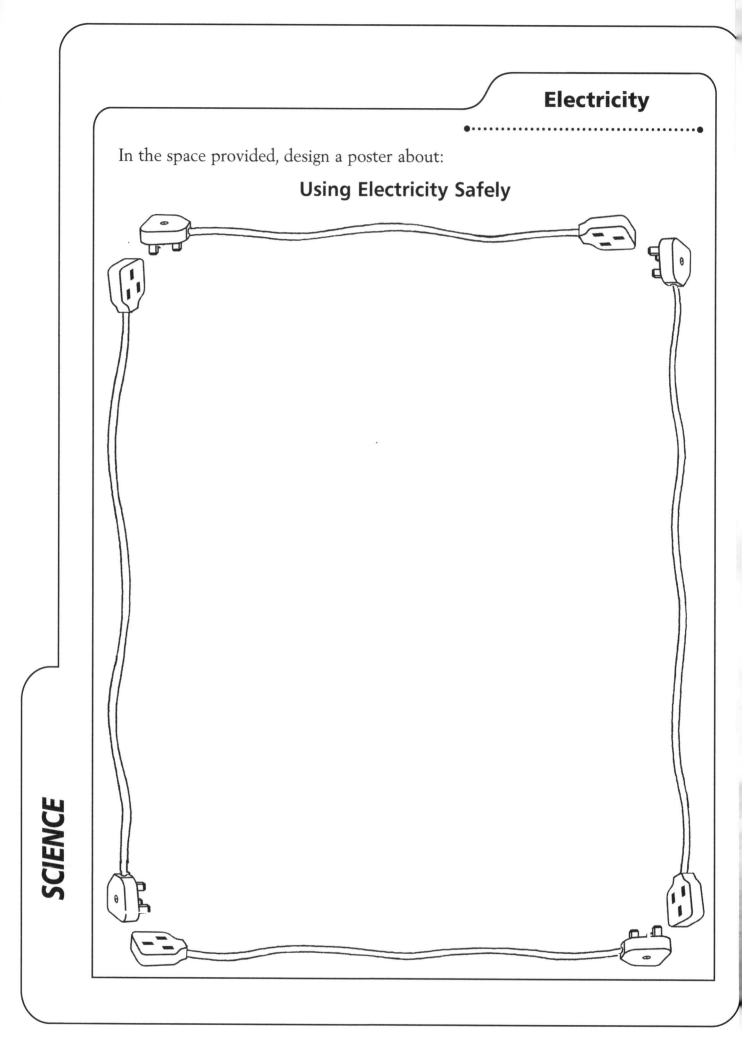

In the space provided, design a poster about:

Using Electricity Safely

Brilliant Publications

Timely Tasks for Fast Finishers 9–11 Year Olds

SCIENCE

Optical illusions

Look closely at the pictures below. Briefly describe what you see.

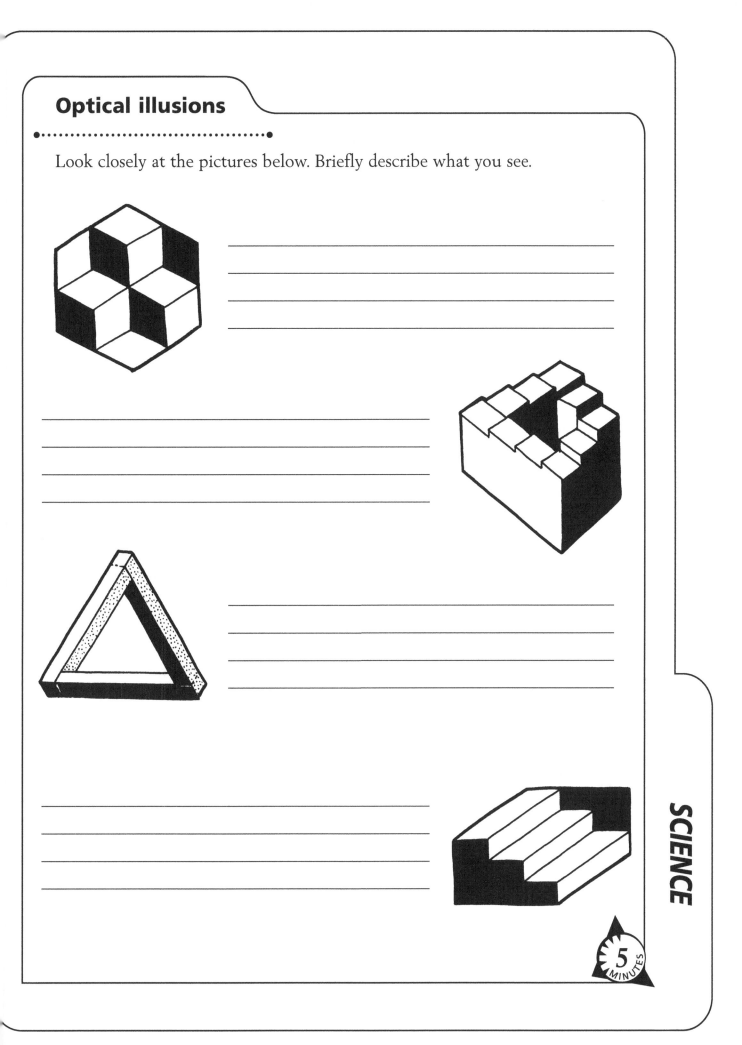

Brilliant Publications

This page may be reproduced by the original purchaser for non-commercial classroom use.

Timely Tasks for Fast Finishers 9–11 Year Olds

© Blake Publishing

53

SCIENCE

Life cycles

10 MINUTES

Choose a creature such as a silkworm, frog, butterfly or mosquito.

Using diagrams, explain and describe its life cycle.

Description

_____

_____

_____

_____

_____

_____

Use another sheet of paper if you run out of space.

Needs and wants

'Needs' are thing we must have in order to live. 'Wants' are not necessary for life, but they make life more satisfying.

Look at the pictures below. Write what each person would wish for. Then say whether what they are wishing for is a 'need' or a 'want'.

_____   _____   _____

_____   _____   _____

5 MINUTES

SCIENCE

54

Brilliant Publications

This page may be reproduced by the original purchaser for non-commercial classroom use.

Timely Tasks for Fast Finishers 9–11 Year Olds

© Blake Publishing

Which role?

Of all the possible roles or occupations in the world, which do you think would be:

Question	Role/occupation	Why?
1. the most exciting?		
2. the most dangerous?		
3. the most boring?		
4. the most difficult?		
5. the strangest?		
6. the most fun?		

In the column 'Why?', explain your answers.

10 MINUTES

What rules?

Make a list of five rules you would make for a school excursion to the zoo.

Next to each rule, write a penalty you would suggest for students who broke it.

Rule	Penalty
1.	
2.	
3.	
4.	
5.	

10 MINUTES

PSHE

© Blake Publishing

Occupations

Look at the following list of occupations. Number them in order from the occupation you think should be paid the most (1) to the one you think should be paid the least (10). Explain why you have placed them in the order you have. Use another sheet of paper if you need more space.

No.	Occupation	Reason for ranking
	Firefighter	
	Dentist	
	Lorry driver	
	Doctor	
	Teacher	
	Refuse collector	
	Police officer	
	Shop assistant	
	Nurse	
	Astronaut	

10 MINUTES

Expectations of others

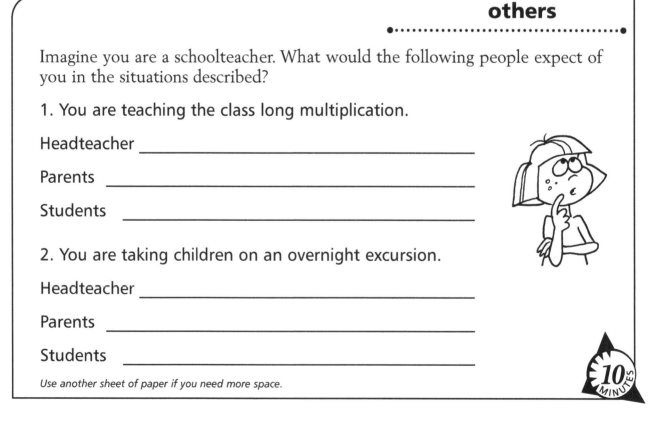

Imagine you are a schoolteacher. What would the following people expect of you in the situations described?

1. You are teaching the class long multiplication.

Headteacher _____

Parents _____

Students _____

2. You are taking children on an overnight excursion.

Headteacher _____

Parents _____

Students _____

Use another sheet of paper if you need more space.

10 MINUTES

PSHE

Brilliant Publications

This page may be reproduced by the original purchaser for non-commercial classroom use.

56

Timely Tasks for Fast Finishers 9–11 Year Olds

© Blake Publishing

Government

Imagine you are the Prime Minister of the UK. Make a list of five things you would do to make the UK a better place in which to live.

1. _____

   _____

2. _____

   _____

3. _____

   _____

4. _____

   _____

5. _____

   _____

5 MINUTES

Problem solving

You have received an invitation to a birthday party. The party will be in December but it is up to you to work out the actual date. See if you can work out the date using the following clues.

1. The party is not on Christmas Eve or New Year's Eve.
2. The sum of the digits in the date is less than 4.
3. The date of the party is not a multiple of 5.
4. The party is not on a Monday.
5. The 'ten' digit is less than the 'units' digit.

SUN	MON	TUE	WED	THURS	FRI	SAT
		1	2	3	4	5
6	7	8	9	10	11	12
13	14	15	16	17	18	19
20	21	22	23	24	25	26
27	28	29	30	31		

5 MINUTES

HUMANITIES

Brilliant Publications

This page may be reproduced by the original purchaser for non-commercial classroom use.

Timely Tasks for Fast Finishers 9–11 Year Olds

© Blake Publishing

57

Conserving fuel

Make a list of ways in which electricity, gas and petrol can be conserved in our homes and daily lives. Use the diagram to write your answers.

Electricity	Gas	Petrol

10 MINUTES

Flags of Great Britain

Design a flag to represent where you live. Describe why you have chosen the things and colours you have.

5 MINUTES

Brilliant Publications

Timely Tasks for Fast Finishers 9–11 Year Olds
© Blake Publishing

General knowledge —1

1. A carnivorous animal eats_____.

2. The young of a deer is called a_____.

3. The primary colours in paint are red, blue and_____.

4. A chihuahua is a kind of_____.

5. The name Bill is short for _____.

6. The planet immediately after Jupiter is_____.

7. The terms 'tee', 'iron' and 'green' are associated with the sport of_____.

8. The _____ is also known as the king of the jungle.

9. A hexagon has _____ sides.

10. Mutton is the meat of a_____.

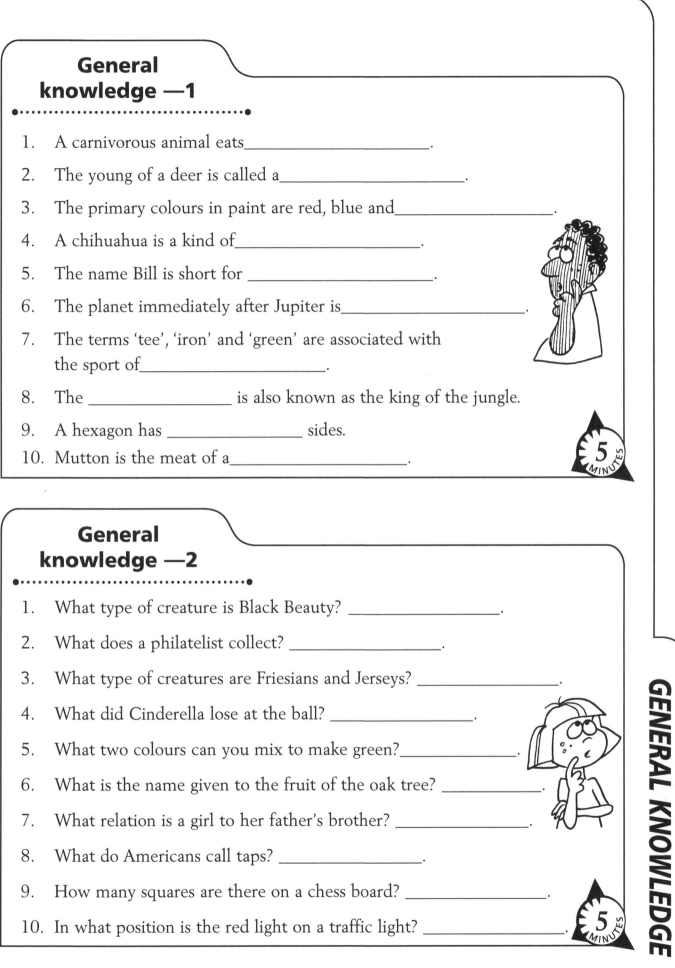

General knowledge —2

1. What type of creature is Black Beauty? _____.

2. What does a philatelist collect? _____.

3. What type of creatures are Friesians and Jerseys? _____.

4. What did Cinderella lose at the ball? _____.

5. What two colours can you mix to make green?_____.

6. What is the name given to the fruit of the oak tree? _____.

7. What relation is a girl to her father's brother? _____.

8. What do Americans call taps? _____.

9. How many squares are there on a chess board? _____.

10. In what position is the red light on a traffic light? _____.

GENERAL KNOWLEDGE

Brilliant Publications

This page may be reproduced by the original purchaser for non-commercial classroom use.

Timely Tasks for Fast Finishers 9–11 Year Olds

© Blake Publishing

59

English

Page 4
Tricky proverbs
1. A small leak will sink a great ship.
2. Every cloud has a silver lining.
3. Great oaks from little acorns grow.
4. A friend in need is a friend indeed.

Page 5
Meanings
1. No
2. No
3. Yes
4. X
5. Yes
6. Yes
7. X
8. No
9. Yes
10. X
11. Yes
12. Yes
13. Yes
14. No

Letterbox
1. 5
2. T
3. E
4. 6
5. 4 and 5
6. Meat, mate, team, tame

Page 6
Scrambled dorws!
1. empty
2. wheel
3. smile
4. found
5. daisy
6. camel
7. fever
8. party
9. habit
10. storm
11. bacon
12. group

13. horse
14. speed
15. denim/mined
16. angry
17. mouth
18. write
19. train
20. beetle

Arithmetic
1. mate
2. mare
3. chair
4. tame
5. team
6. heart
7. cream
8. rat
9. tear

Page 7
Word play
1. fat / plump
2. shed / barn
3. boat / ship
4. bare / bald
5. kill / slaughter

Word quiz
ape, ate, age, ale, are
be, bet, beg, beat, bear, bean, beam
eat, ear
fen, few, feat, fear, fame, fate, fare
gem, get, gel, gear, game, great
he, hem, hen, hew, her, heat, hear, heal, heap
let, leg, lean, leaf, leap, lame, lane, late
meat, mean, mane, meal
new, net, neat, nape, name
peat, pea, peg, pen, pet, pear
ten, tea, team, teal, tear, tame, tape, tare, table, them, then
we, wet, web, wean, wear, wheat
This is just a start – you will probably find many more!

Page 8
Mystery words
HALLOWEEN

Clues:

1.	3L	2A	6W	9N
2.	1H	7E	7E	4L
3.	1H	5O	3L	8E
4.	6W	1H	2A	3L 8E

Cross it out!
1. hearse
2. nought
3. centre
4. draper
5. sister

Page 9
Missing EEs
1. eagle
2. jewel
3. fence
4. general
5. enemy
6. velvet
7. perfect
8. coffee

Missing creatures
1. magpie
2. ostrich
3. monkey
4. parrot
5. porcupine
6. cat
7. trout
8. mouse

Page 10
Shrinking words
startling
starting
staring
string
sting
sing
sin
in
I
snowing
sowing
swing
sing (or wing)
sin (or win)
in
I

Brilliant Publications

ANSWERS

Multiple poems

"The ploughman homeward plods his weary way."

1. The ploughman plods his weary way homeward.
2. The weary ploughman plods his way homeward.
3. The ploughman, weary, plods his way homeward.
4. The ploughman plods homeward his weary way.
5. Homeward plods the ploughman his weary way.
6. His weary way homeward plods the ploughman.
7. His way homeward plods the weary ploughman.

Sporting words
Hockey

Page 11
Swap shops
Shoes

Therein
1. the
2. there
3. he
4. her
5. in
6. then
7. here
8. hen

You may find others.

Page 12
Scrapbook
1. cook, 2. sock,
3. crab, 4. oak, 5. boar,
6. cobra, 7. rock, 8. car,
9. park, 10. cop,
11. crook, 12. carp

What's it say?
Video Cassette Recorder, Liquid Crystal Display, Greenwich Mean Time, Heavy Goods Vehicle, National Aeronautics (and) Space Administration, Do-it-Yourself, Old-age Pensioner, Anti-social Behaviour Order.

Page 13
Mixed-up meals
sausages, mustard, margarine, coffee, steak, crumpets, biscuits, sauce, cheese, bananas

Connections
1. plant, 2. hornet,
3. cheese, 4. nephew,
5. vinegar, 6. adder,
7. terrier, 8. hay,
9. heart, 10. ice

Page 14
Sayings
1. The long arm of the law. 2. One good turn deserves another. 3. Faster than a speeding bullet. 4. By hook or by crook. 5. A rolling stone gathers no moss. 6. Who dares wins.

Small words
1. ant, 2. ill, 3. test,
4. chin, 5. pear, 6. tent

Page 15
Country cultures
turban India,
castanets Spain,
Zulu South Africa,
loch Scotland,
taco Mexico,
spaghetti Italy,
moussaka Greece,
kiwi New Zealand

Word changes
Diet dirt dart cart CARE;
Walls wills wiles tiles tiler TIGER

Page 16
Mix 'n' match
turnip, python, almond, wallet, jumper, desert, twelve, marble, stable, banana

Spell well
anchor, envelope, assistant, general, already, leopard, written, frown, beret, soldier, answer, lizard, easily, robust, cemetery, danger, careful, friend.

Page 17
Missing vowels
chemist, surveyor, builder, architect, watchmaker, bricklayer, teacher, jeweller, carpenter, plumber, farmer, dentist, driving instructor, solicitor, hairdresser

Words for words

Large: gargantuan, extensive, monstrous, huge, gigantic, massive, vast, spacious, mammoth, giant, colossal

Small: wee, meagre, puny, minute, shrunken, dwarfish, slight, shrivelled, trivial, tiny, stunted

Spoke: bellowed, enquired, argued, groaned, grumbled, recited, declared, replied, complained, stammered

Page 18
Body parts
eye, ear, toe, arm, leg, lip, lid, hip, rib, fat

More small words
fragile, factory, dreary, pink, million, elastic, orchestra, enamel

---

Maths

Page 19
Bull's-eye
4 darts
32/18/32/18
5 darts
48/14/14/12/12
6 darts
32/18/14/12/12/12

Tricky triangles
20

Multiple patterns
1. 111
2. 222
3. 333
4. 444
5. 555

Page 20

Squared up

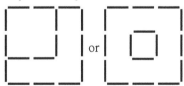

Brilliant Publications

This page may be reproduced by the original purchaser for non-commercial classroom use.

Timely Tasks for Fast Finishers 9–11 Year Olds

© Blake Publishing

61

Teaser

20

Totals

1. 23
2. 41
3. 16
4. 75

Page 21
Number square quiz

1. 3
2. 4
3. 3
4. 6
5. 2

Page 22
Number facts

1. 19
2. 20
3. 42
4. 70

Line divisions

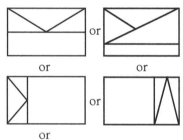

Page 23
Quick think

1. 24½
2. 95
3. 37
4. 135
5. 29
6. 182
7. 1,956
8. 344
9. 54¼
10. 80
11. 75
12. 92

Number diamonds

2	4	5	7
1	8	3	6

Page 24
Sale time

1. flour   £1.45
2. bread   £1.45
3. margarine   £2.75
4. detergent   £2.40
5. sausages   £2.60
6. butter   £1.60

Target practice

30

$(2 \times 5) + 20 = 30$
$(3 \times 5) + 15 = 30$
$(2 \times 12) + 6 = 30$
$(3 \times 8) + 6 = 30$

Page 25
Magic squares

3	3	6
7	4	1
2	5	5

Stop and think

5 : R, G, A
     G, A, R
     G, R, A
     A, R, G
     A, G, R

Odd one out

Odd one out is 34. All the other numbers are evenly divisible by 3.

Puzzle?

They are all squares.

Page 26
Number quiz

1. f
2. e
3. d
4. a
5. g
6. c
7. 9020
8. 21432

Clocking it up

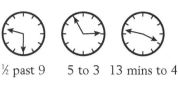

½ past 9   5 to 3   13 mins to 4

¼ to 4   ¼ to 6   ¼ to 6

Page 27
Colour squares

Red 36 / Light Blue 41 / Green 13, 17, 19 / Pink 44 / Yellow 1 / Brown 40 / Dark Blue 49 / Black 23.

Magic squares

All lines and rows add up to 19998.

Page 28
Cross tots

The totals across and down should read 5278.

Circling round

1. $5 + 7 + 5 + 3$
2. $6 + 8 + 10 + 11$
3. $11 + 8 + 12 + 7 + 8$
4. $17 + 8 + 12 + 10 + 11$
5. $15 + 20 + 15 + 25$
6. $25 + 5 + 60 + 5 + 15$
7. $10 + 1 + 30 + 15 + 12$
8. $12 + 45 + 12 + 30 + 25$

Page 29
Dropping off

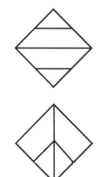

ANSWERS

62

Brilliant Publications

This page may be reproduced by the original purchaser for non-commercial classroom use.

Timely Tasks for Fast Finishers 9–11 Year Olds
© Blake Publishing

More magic squares

a

5	0	4
2	3	4
2	6	1

b

3	3	6
7	4	1
2	5	5

c

8	3	4
1	5	9
6	7	2

d

8	7	3
1	6	11
9	5	4

e

5	13	3
5	7	9
11	1	9

f

9	15	6
7	10	13
14	5	11

Page 30
Number quiz
1. 3, 2. 101, 3. 20 000, 4. 9,
5. 9, 6. 13, 7. 24, 8. 40,
9. 12, 10. 2

Factor fun
b. 10 / 3, 5, 2; c. 10 / 5, 2, 5;
d. 7, 10 / 7, 5, 2; e. 2, 50 / 2,
10, 5; f. 8 / 7, 4, 2

Page 31
Twenty-one is sharp
(hash sign)

Number cross
Across 1. 444, 4. 47, 6. 2608, 7.
84, 8. 63, 9. 55, 10. 2544, 13.
32, 14. 659

Down 1. 42, 2. 4685, 3. 404, 5.
733, 8. 6245, 9. 563, 11. 56, 12.
49

Page 32
Boxing on
All the boxes should be
coloured in.

Spotty
Y

What number?
1. 12, 2. 36, 3. 246,
4. 195, 5. 22

Page 33
Signing on
1. $3 \times 2 + 4 = 10$
2. $8 + 8 - 6 = 10$
3. $20 \div 5 + 4 = 8$
4. $12 - 4 \times 2 = 16$
5. $14 + 6 + 10 = 30$
6. $20 - 4 - 6 = 10$
7. $5 \times 3 + 5 = 20$
8. $30 \div 6 + 12 = 17$
9. $40 - 20 - 20 = 0$
10. $7 + 7 \times 2 = 28$

Shipshapes

1

2

3

4

5

Page 34
What's the end?

1

30
60
50
10
50
300

2

12
48
96
24
12
36

3

70
140
280
780
260
2600

4

750
1500
500
250
125
25

Number words
1. decade, 2. century,
3. tripod, 4. centipede, 5. six,
6. octopus, 7. duet,
8. pair, 9. tricycle,
10. five, 11. 79, 90,
12. bi-plane

Page 35
Picture problem
Tortoise

Thinking

Page 40
Odd one out
1b
2d
3a
4c

Page 42
Picture sayings
1 I understand
2 Over the rainbow
3 Raining cats and dogs
4 Tap dancing

Page 43
Classifying creatures
1a Trituff
1b Gerakaff
1c Zonuff
3. not possible – no such
creature would exist

Page 44
Make a letter
Match the following pieces in
the following order to make the
letter 'G'.
h, b, e
i, j, a
c, k, g

Page 46
Match up
a – g
b – d
c – f
e – h

Circle sums
$5 \times 4 \div 2 = 10$
$6 \times 9 \div 3 = 18$
$5 + 7 - 8 = 4$
= = =
6   6   13

Brilliant Publications

This page may be reproduced by the original purchaser for non-commercial classroom use.

Timely Tasks for Fast Finishers 9–11 Year Olds
© Blake Publishing

63

Page 47
Eye challenges
Each of these is an optical illusion that can exist on paper as a 2D drawing, but cannot be made as a 3D object.

Page 48
Think about it
1   11
2   All of them.
3   11,111
4   K
5   All of them.
6   None – a hole is empty of soil!
7   'To tie mules to.'

Science

Page 49
Our environment—1
These are some suggestions—you may come up with other ideas:

No larvae = less food for fish and possibly frogs = less food for waterbirds that eat fish, frogs and tadpoles. Less life in the pond may cause it to become stagnant.

The oil will also prevent air from entering the water. It will choke pond life and get into the fur, feathers and digestive systems of the birds and animals that come to the pond to drink and look for food.

Page 50
Our environment—2
How the environment is being affected:

Smoke and car exhaust are polluting the air. Trees have been destroyed, perhaps because the air is so polluted. The ground looks very bare and the wind is blowing away the topsoil.

Waste from the factory is being emptied into the river, killing wildlife.

Page 51
Our bodies
rib/chest, upper torso
humerus/arm
radius/forearm (shorter and thicker)
ulna/forearm (longer and thinner)
patella/knee
tarsus/ankle
carpus/wrist
fibula/lower leg (on the outside)
tibia/lower leg (inside)
stapes/ear
clavicle/collar bone
femur/leg
skull/head
metatarsal/foot

Page 54
Needs and wants
• Person in desert dying of thirst—water/need.
• Hungry girl looking at cakes to eat—cakes/want.
• Cricketer coming out to bat, starting to rain—sunny weather/want.
• Boy in a vest in the freezing cold—something warm to wear/need.
• Shipwrecked person on island—food, water, shelter and company/need.
• Girl dreaming of a bicycle—bicycle/want.

Humanities

Page 57
Problem solving
Saturday, 12 December

Page 58
Conserving fuel
Electricity – turn off lights, use energy-saving lighting, wash clothes in cold water, have a well-insulated house and dress warmly so that you don't need to use as much heating.

Gas – wash clothes in cold water, have a well-insulated house and dress warmly so that you don't need to use as much heating.

Petrol – walk, catch the bus, share lifts, ride a bike.

General knowledge

Page 59
General knowledge – 1
1.   meat
2.   fawn
3.   yellow
4.   dog
5.   William
6.   Saturn
7.   golf
8.   lion
9.   six
10.   sheep

General knowledge – 2
1.   horse
2.   postage stamps
3.   milking cows
4.   glass slipper
5.   blue and yellow
6.   acorn
7.   niece
8.   faucets
9.   64
10.   at the top

ANSWERS

Brilliant Publications
Timely Tasks for Fast Finishers 9–11 Year Olds
© Blake Publishing